OFFICIAL SQA PAST PAPERS WITH ANSWERS

STANDARD GRADE | CREDIT

CHEMISTRY
2007-2011

Publisher's Note

We are delighted to bring you the 2011 Past Papers and you will see that we have changed the format from previous editions. As part of our environmental awareness strategy, we have attempted to make these new editions as sustainable as possible.
To do this, we have printed on white paper and bound the answer sections into the book. This not only allows us to use significantly less paper but we are also, for the first time, able to source all the materials from sustainable sources.

We hope you like the new editions and by purchasing this product, you are not only supporting an independent Scottish publishing company but you are also, in the International Year of Forests, not contributing to the destruction of the world's forests.

Thank you for your support and please see the following websites for more information to support the above statement –

www.fsc-uk.org

www.loveforests.com

© Scottish Qualifications Authority
All rights reserved. Copying prohibited. No part of this publication may be reproduced, stored in a retrieval system, or transmitted in any form or by any means, electronic, mechanical, photocopying, recording or otherwise.

First exam published in 2007.
Published by Bright Red Publishing Ltd, 6 Stafford Street, Edinburgh EH3 7AU
tel: 0131 220 5804 fax: 0131 220 6710 info@brightredpublishing.co.uk www.brightredpublishing.co.uk

ISBN 978-1-84948-162-5

A CIP Catalogue record for this book is available from the British Library.

Bright Red Publishing is grateful to the copyright holders, as credited on the final page of the Question Section, for permission to use their material. Every effort has been made to trace the copyright holders and to obtain their permission for the use of copyright material. Bright Red Publishing will be happy to receive information allowing us to rectify any error or omission in future editions.

STANDARD GRADE | CREDIT

2007

[BLANK PAGE]

C

FOR OFFICIAL USE

KU   PS

Total Marks

0500/402

NATIONAL
QUALIFICATIONS
2007

THURSDAY, 10 MAY
10.50 AM – 12.20 PM

CHEMISTRY
STANDARD GRADE
Credit Level

Fill in these boxes and read what is printed below.

Full name of centre

Town

Forename(s)

Surname

Date of birth

Day Month Year   Scottish candidate number   Number of seat

1 All questions should be attempted.

2 Necessary data will be found in the Data Booklet provided for Chemistry at Standard Grade and Intermediate 2.

3 The questions may be answered in any order but all answers are to be written in this answer book, and must be written clearly and legibly in ink.

4 Rough work, if any should be necessary, as well as the fair copy, is to be written in this book.

Rough work should be scored through when the fair copy has been written.

5 Additional space for answers and rough work will be found at the end of the book.

6 The size of the space provided for an answer should not be taken as an indication of how much to write. It is not necessary to use all the space.

7 Before leaving the examination room you must give this book to the invigilator. If you do not, you may lose all the marks for this paper.

SCOTTISH
QUALIFICATIONS
AUTHORITY

©

PART 1

In Questions 1 to 9 of this part of the paper, an answer is given by circling the appropriate letter (or letters) in the answer grid provided.

In some questions, two letters are required for full marks.

If more than the correct number of answers is given, marks will be deducted.

A total of 20 marks is available in this part of the paper.

SAMPLE QUESTION

A CH_4	B H_2	C CO_2
D CO	E C_2H_5OH	F C

(a) Identify the hydrocarbon.

Ⓐ	B	C
D	E	F

The one correct answer to part (a) is A. This should be circled.

(b) Identify the **two** elements.

A	Ⓑ	C
D	E	Ⓕ

As indicated in this question, there are **two** correct answers to part (b). These are B and F. Both answers are circled.

If, after you have recorded your answer, you decide that you have made an error and wish to make a change, you should cancel the original answer and circle the answer you now consider to be correct. Thus, in part (a), if you want to change an answer A to an answer D, your answer sheet would look like this:

A̶	B	C
Ⓓ	E	F

If you want to change back to an answer which has already been scored out, you should enter a tick (✓) in the box of the answer of your choice, thus:

✓A̶	B	C
D̶	E	F

1.

Testing gases

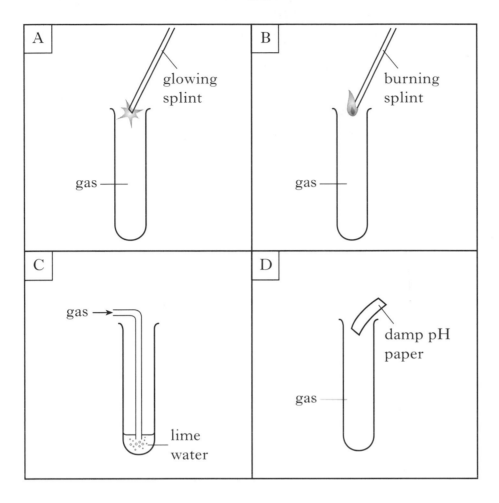

(a) Identify the test for oxygen gas.

A	B
C	D

(b) Identify a test for ammonia gas.

A	B
C	D

1

1

(2)

[Turn over

Marks

KU   PS

2. Zinc and magnesium both react with dilute hydrochloric acid.

A	B	C
20 °C zinc lump 1 mol/l hydrochloric acid	20 °C magnesium lump 1 mol/l hydrochloric acid	30 °C magnesium lump 1 mol/l hydrochloric acid
D	**E**	**F**
30 °C zinc powder 2 mol/l hydrochloric acid	40 °C magnesium powder 2 mol/l hydrochloric acid	40 °C zinc lump 2 mol/l hydrochloric acid

(a) Identify the experiment with the **slowest** rate of reaction.

A	B	C
D	E	F

1

(b) Identify the **two** experiments which could be used to investigate the effect of temperature on the rate of reaction.

A	B	C
D	E	F

1

(2)

Marks | KU | PS

3. Distillation of crude oil produces several fractions.

Fraction	Number of carbon atoms per molecule
A	1–4
B	4–10
C	10–16
D	16–20
E	20+

crude oil ⟶

(a) Identify the fraction which is used to tar roads.

A
B
C
D
E

1

(b) Identify the fraction with the lowest boiling point.

A
B
C
D
E

1

(2)

[Turn over

Marks | KU | PS

4. The structural formulae for some hydrocarbons are shown below.

A	B	C
CH₃ H | | C = C | | H H	H H \ / C H–C — C–H H H	H CH₃ | | H–C — C–H | | CH₃ H
D	E	F
H H | | H–C–C–H | | H–C–C–H | | H H	CH₃ H | | H–C — C–H | | H H	CH₃ H | | C = C | | H CH₃

(a) Identify the hydrocarbon which could be used to make poly(butene).

A	B	C
D	E	F

1

(b) Identify the **two** hydrocarbons with the general formula C_nH_{2n} which do **not** react quickly with hydrogen.

A	B	C
D	E	F

1

(2)

Marks | KU | PS

5. The table contains information about some substances.

Substance	Melting point/ °C	Boiling point/ °C	Conducts as a solid	Conducts as a liquid
A	1700	2230	no	no
B	605	1305	no	yes
C	−13	77	no	no
D	801	1413	no	yes
E	181	1347	yes	yes
F	−39	357	yes	yes

(a) Identify the substance which exists as covalent molecules.

A
B
C
D
E
F

1

(b) Identify the metal which is liquid at 25 °C.

A
B
C
D
E
F

1

(2)

[Turn over

Marks | KU | PS

6. Equations are used to represent chemical reactions.

A	$Sn(s) \longrightarrow Sn^{2+}(aq) + 2e^-$
B	$Cu^{2+}(aq) + 2e^- \longrightarrow Cu(s)$
C	$H^+(aq) + OH^-(aq) \longrightarrow H_2O(\ell)$
D	$2Mg(s) + O_2(g) \longrightarrow 2MgO(s)$
E	$SO_2(g) + H_2O(\ell) \longrightarrow 2H^+(aq) + SO_3^{2-}(aq)$

(a) Identify the equation which represents the formation of acid rain.

A
B
C
D
E

1

(b) Identify the equation which represents neutralisation.

A
B
C
D
E

1

(c) Identify the **two** equations in which a substance is oxidised.

A
B
C
D
E

2

(4)

Marks | KU | PS

7. A student made some statements about the particles found in atoms.

A	It has a positive charge.
B	It has a negative charge.
C	It has a relative mass of almost zero.
D	It has a relative mass of 1.
E	It is found inside the nucleus.
F	It is found outside the nucleus.

Identify the **two** statements which apply to **both** a proton and a neutron.

A
B
C
D
E
F

(2)

8. A student made some statements about the reaction of silver(I) oxide with excess dilute hydrochloric acid.

A	The concentration of hydrogen ions increases.
B	Carbon dioxide gas is produced.
C	An insoluble salt is produced.
D	Hydrogen gas is produced.
E	Water is produced.

Identify the **two** correct statements.

A
B
C
D
E

(2)

Page nine **[Turn over**

Marks | KU | PS

9. When two different electrodes are joined in a cell, a chemical reaction takes place and a voltage is produced.

sodium chloride solution and ferroxyl indicator

	Electrode A	*Electrode B*
A	magnesium	iron
B	iron	carbon
C	iron	aluminium
D	iron	copper
E	lead	iron

Which **two** pairs of electrodes will produce a flow of electrons in the same direction as shown in the diagram and would produce a blue colour around electrode **A**?

You may wish to use the data booklet to help you.

A
B
C
D
E

(2)

[Turn over for Part 2 on *Page twelve*

Marks | KU | PS

PART 2

A total of 40 marks is available in this part of the paper.

10. A sample of silver was found to contain two isotopes, $^{107}_{47}Ag$ and $^{109}_{47}Ag$.

(a) This sample of silver has an average atomic mass of 108.

What does this indicate about the amount of each isotope in this sample?

_____

_____

1

(b) Complete the table to show the number of each type of particle in a $^{107}_{47}Ag^+$ ion.

Particle	Number
proton	
neutron	
electron	

2

(c) Silver can be displaced from a solution of silver(I) nitrate.

$$AgNO_3(aq) + Cu(s) \longrightarrow Ag(s) + Cu(NO_3)_2(aq)$$

(i) Balance this equation.

1

(ii) Name a metal which would **not** displace silver from silver(I) nitrate.

You may wish to use the data booklet to help you.

_____

1

(5)

Marks

11. Alkanoic acids are a family of compounds which contain the $-C\diagup_{O-H}^{\diagup O}$ group.

The **full** structural formulae for the first three members are shown.

methanoic acid

ethanoic acid

propanoic acid

(a) Draw the **full** structural formula for the alkanoic acid containing 4 carbon atoms.

1

(b) The table gives information on some alkanoic acids.

Acid	Boiling point/ °C
methanoic acid	101
ethanoic acid	118
propanoic acid	141
butanoic acid	164

(i) Using this information, make a general statement linking the boiling point to the number of carbon atoms.

_____

_____

_____ 1

(ii) Predict the boiling point of pentanoic acid.

_____ °C 1

(3)

[Turn over

Marks

12. Ammonia is made when nitrogen and hydrogen react together.

The table below shows the percentage yields obtained when nitrogen and hydrogen react at different pressures.

Pressure/atmospheres	Percentage yield of ammonia
25	28
50	40
100	53
200	67
400	80

(a) Draw a line graph of percentage yield against pressure.

Use appropriate scales to fill most of the graph paper.

(Additional graph paper, if required, will be found on page 27.)

2

(b) Use your graph to estimate the percentage yield of ammonia at 150 atmospheres.

1

12. **(continued)**

(*c*) Ammonia can be produced in the lab by heating an ammonium compound with soda lime.

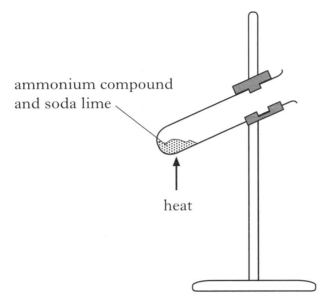

ammonium compound
and soda lime

heat

In order to produce ammonia, what **type** of compound must soda lime be?

_____

1

(4)

[Turn over

Marks | KU | PS

13. Starch and sucrose can be hydrolysed to produce simple sugars.

Chromatography is a technique which can be used to identify the sugars produced.

Samples of known sugar solutions are spotted on the base line. The solvent travels up the paper carrying spots of sugars at different rates.

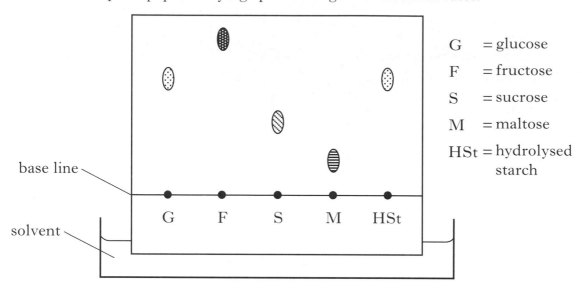

G   = glucose
F   = fructose
S   = sucrose
M   = maltose
HSt = hydrolysed starch

The diagram above shows that **only glucose** is produced when starch is hydrolysed.

(a) The chromatogram below can be used to identify the simple sugars produced when sucrose is hydrolysed.

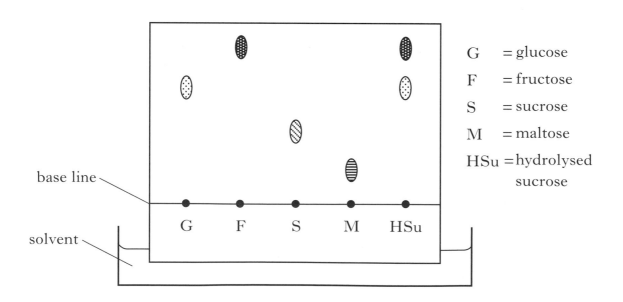

G   = glucose
F   = fructose
S   = sucrose
M   = maltose
HSu = hydrolysed sucrose

Name the sugars produced when sucrose is hydrolysed.

_____

1

DO NOT
WRITE IN
THIS
MARGIN

Marks | KU | PS

13. (continued)

(*b*) What **type** of substance, present in the digestive system, acts as a catalyst in the hydrolysis of sucrose?

_____

1

(2)

[**Turn over**

Marks

14. Cars made from steel can be protected from rusting in a number of ways.

(a) Circle the correct word to complete the sentence below.

Steel does not rust when attached to the $\begin{Bmatrix} \text{negative} \\ \text{positive} \end{Bmatrix}$ terminal of a car battery.

1

(b) The steel body of the car can be coated by dipping it in molten zinc.

(i) What name is given to this process?

_____

1

(ii) Explain why the steel does **not** rust even when the zinc coating is scratched.

_____

_____

_____

1

(3)

Marks   KU   PS

15. The atoms in a chlorine molecule are held together by a covalent bond. A covalent bond is a shared pair of electrons.

The chlorine molecule can be represented as

                    ● = electron

(a) Showing **all** outer electrons, draw a similar diagram to represent a molecule of hydrogen chloride, HCl.

1

(b) In forming covalent bonds, why do atoms share electrons?

_____

_____

_____   1

(2)

[Turn over

16. Ethanol is the alcohol found in alcoholic drinks.

It can be produced as shown in the diagram.

— cotton wool

— glucose solution
and
yeast at 30 °C

(a) (i) Name the type of chemical reaction taking place in the flask.

_____ 1

(ii) What would happen to the rate of the reaction if the experiment above was repeated at 50 °C?

_____ 1

(b) In industry, alcohols can be produced from alkenes as shown in the example below.

(i) Name the type of chemical reaction taking place.

_____ 1

Marks | KU | PS

16. **(b) (continued)**

    (ii)   What **term** is used to describe a pair of alcohols like propan-1-ol and propan-2-ol?

_____

1

    (iii)   Propan-1-ol and propan-2-ol have different boiling points.

           Name the process which could be used to separate a mixture of these alcohols.

_____

1

(5)

[Turn over

Marks | KU | PS

17. The table contains information on minerals.

Mineral	Formula
cinnabar	HgS
fluorite	CaF_2
gibbsite	$Al(OH)_3$
haematite	Fe_2O_3
zinc blende	ZnS

(a) State the chemical name for zinc blende.

_____   1

(b) Name the salt formed when gibbsite reacts with dilute hydrochloric acid.

_____   1

(c) Calculate the percentage, by mass, of calcium in fluorite (CaF_2).

Show your working clearly.

_____ %   2

(d) Iron metal can be extracted from haematite (Fe_2O_3) by heating with carbon monoxide. Carbon dioxide is also produced.

Write an equation, using **symbols** and **formulae**, for this reaction.

There is no need to balance it.

_____   1

(e) Name a metal which can be extracted from its ore by heat alone.

_____   1

(6)

Marks

18. Nylon is a polymer with many uses.

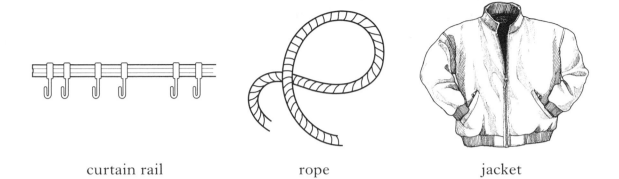

curtain rail   rope   jacket

(a) Nylon is a thermoplastic polymer.

What does thermoplastic mean?

_____

_____   1

(b) Nylon is a polymer made from two different monomers as shown.

During the polymerisation reaction, water is also produced.

Suggest a name for this **type** of polymerisation.

_____   1
(2)

[Turn over

Marks | KU | PS

19. Many ionic compounds are coloured.

Compound	Colour
nickel(II) nitrate	green
nickel(II) sulphate	green
potassium permanganate	purple
potassium sulphate	colourless

(a) Using the information in the table, state the colour of the potassium ion.

_____   1

(b) Write the **ionic** formula for nickel(II) nitrate.

_____   1

(c) A student set up the following experiment to investigate the colour of the ions in copper(II) chromate.

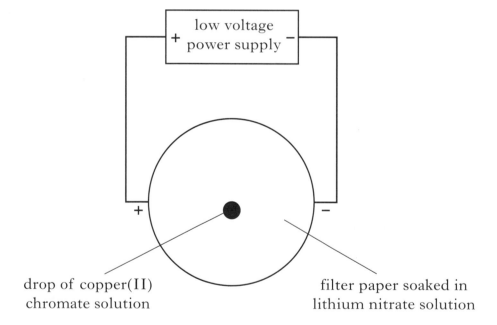

drop of copper(II)
chromate solution

filter paper soaked in
lithium nitrate solution

The student made the following observation.

Observation
yellow colour moves to the positive electrode
blue colour moves to the negative electrode

DO NOT
WRITE IN
THIS
MARGIN

Marks | KU | PS

19. (*c*) (continued)

(i) State the colour of the chromate ion.

_____

1

(ii) Lithium nitrate solution is used as the electrolyte.

What is the purpose of an electrolyte?

_____

_____

_____

1

(iii) Suggest why lithium phosphate can **not** be used as the electrolyte in this experiment.

You may wish to use the data booklet to help you.

_____

_____

_____

1

(5)

[Turn over

Marks | KU | PS

20. Indigestion is caused by excess acid in the stomach. Indigestion remedies containing calcium carbonate neutralise some of this acid.

Christine carried out an experiment to find the mass of calcium carbonate required to neutralise a dilute hydrochloric acid solution.

She added calcium carbonate until all the acid had been used up.

50 cm³ of 4 mol/l hydrochloric acid

(a) Calculate the number of moles of dilute hydrochloric acid used in the experiment.

_____ mol   **1**

(b) The equation for the reaction is

$$CaCO_3(s) + 2HCl(aq) \longrightarrow CaCl_2(aq) + H_2O(\ell) + CO_2(g)$$

(i) Using your answer from part (a), calculate the number of moles of calcium carbonate required to neutralise the dilute hydrochloric acid.

_____ mol   **1**

(ii) Using your answer from part (b)(i), calculate the **mass** of calcium carbonate ($CaCO_3$) required to neutralise the acid.

_____ g   **1**

(3)

[END OF QUESTION PAPER]

ADDITIONAL SPACE FOR ANSWERS

ADDITIONAL GRAPH PAPER FOR QUESTION 12(*a*)

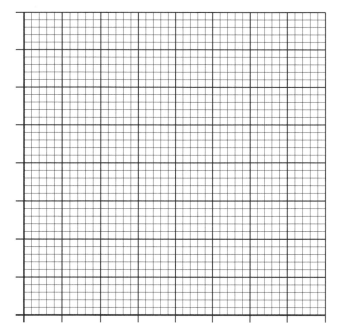

[BLANK PAGE]

2008

[BLANK PAGE]

C

FOR OFFICIAL USE

	KU	PS
Total Marks		

0500/402

NATIONAL
QUALIFICATIONS
2008

THURSDAY, 1 MAY
10.50 AM – 12.20 PM

CHEMISTRY
STANDARD GRADE
Credit Level

Fill in these boxes and read what is printed below.

Full name of centre

Town

Forename(s)

Surname

Date of birth

Day Month Year   Scottish candidate number   Number of seat

1 All questions should be attempted.

2 Necessary data will be found in the Data Booklet provided for Chemistry at Standard Grade and Intermediate 2.

3 The questions may be answered in any order but all answers are to be written in this answer book, and must be written clearly and legibly in ink.

4 Rough work, if any should be necessary, as well as the fair copy, is to be written in this book.

Rough work should be scored through when the fair copy has been written.

5 Additional space for answers and rough work will be found at the end of the book.

6 The size of the space provided for an answer should not be taken as an indication of how much to write. It is not necessary to use all the space.

7 Before leaving the examination room you must give this book to the invigilator. If you do not, you may lose all the marks for this paper.

PART 1

In Questions 1 to 9 of this part of the paper, an answer is given by circling the appropriate letter (or letters) in the answer grid provided.

In some questions, two letters are required for full marks.

If more than the correct number of answers is given, marks will be deducted.

A total of 20 marks is available in this part of the paper.

SAMPLE QUESTION

A CH_4	B H_2	C CO_2
D CO	E C_2H_5OH	F C

(a) Identify the hydrocarbon.

Ⓐ	B	C
D	E	F

The one correct answer to part (a) is A. This should be circled.

(b) Identify the **two** elements.

A	Ⓑ	C
D	E	Ⓕ

As indicated in this question, there are **two** correct answers to part (b). These are B and F. Both answers are circled.

If, after you have recorded your answer, you decide that you have made an error and wish to make a change, you should cancel the original answer and circle the answer you now consider to be correct. Thus, in part (a), if you want to change an answer A to an answer D, your answer sheet would look like this:

A̶	B	C
Ⓓ	E	F

If you want to change back to an answer which has already been scored out, you should enter a tick (✓) in the box of the answer of your choice, thus:

✓A̶	B	C
D̶	E	F

Marks | KU | PS

1. The formulae of some gases are shown in the grid.

A	B	C
H_2	N_2	CO
D	**E**	**F**
O_2	CO_2	NO_2

(a) Identify the toxic gas produced during the burning of plastics.

A	B	C
D	E	F

1

(b) Identify the gas which makes up approximately 80% of air.

A	B	C
D	E	F

1

(c) Identify the gas used up during respiration.

A	B	C
D	E	F

1

(3)

[Turn over

Marks KU PS

2. A student carried out several experiments with metals and acids.

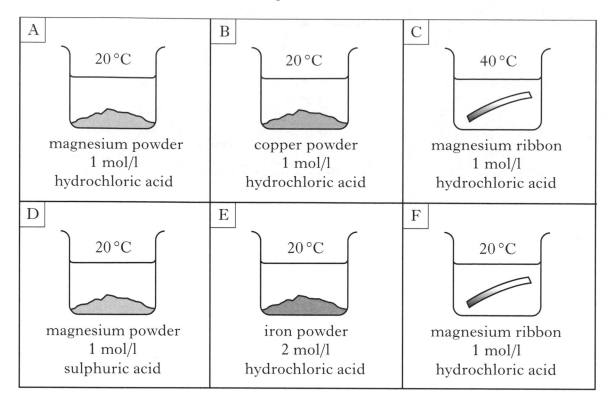

A 20 °C magnesium powder 1 mol/l hydrochloric acid	**B** 20 °C copper powder 1 mol/l hydrochloric acid	**C** 40 °C magnesium ribbon 1 mol/l hydrochloric acid
D 20 °C magnesium powder 1 mol/l sulphuric acid	**E** 20 °C iron powder 2 mol/l hydrochloric acid	**F** 20 °C magnesium ribbon 1 mol/l hydrochloric acid

(a) Identify the **two** experiments which could be compared to show the effect of particle size on reaction rate.

A	B	C
D	E	F

1

(b) Identify the experiment in which **no** reaction would take place.

A	B	C
D	E	F

1

(2)

Marks | KU | PS

3. The grid shows the structural formulae of some hydrocarbons.

A	B	C
H $-$ C $-$ C $-$ H (with H atoms above and below each carbon)	triangular ring of three C atoms each with two H	C $=$ C (with H above and below each carbon)

D	E	F
CH_3, H on C $=$ C with H, H below	H $-$ C $-$ C $-$ C $-$ H with CH_3 above and CH_3 below middle carbon	H $-$ C $-$ C $-$ H, H $-$ C $-$ C $-$ H (ring of four carbons)

(a) Identify the **two** hydrocarbons which can polymerise.

A	B	C
D	E	F

1

(b) Identify the **two** hydrocarbons with the general formula C_nH_{2n} which do **not** decolourise bromine solution quickly.

A	B	C
D	E	F

1

(2)

[Turn over

4. The grid shows the names of some oxides.

A	B	C
silicon dioxide	carbon dioxide	sodium oxide
D	**E**	**F**
iron oxide	sulphur dioxide	copper oxide

(a) Identify the **two** oxides which contain transition metals.

You may wish to use the data booklet to help you.

A	B	C
D	E	F

1

(b) Identify the oxide which reacts with water in the atmosphere to produce acid rain.

A	B	C
D	E	F

1

(c) Identify the oxide which, when added to water, produces a solution with a greater concentration of hydroxide ions (OH^-) than hydrogen ions (H^+).

A	B	C
D	E	F

1

(3)

Marks | KU | PS

5. There are different types of chemical reactions.

A	redox
B	precipitation
C	combustion
D	neutralisation
E	displacement

(a) Identify the type of chemical reaction taking place when dilute hydrochloric acid reacts with a carbonate.

A
B
C
D
E

1

(b) Identify the **two** types of chemical reaction represented by the following equation.

$$2Zn(s) + O_2(g) \longrightarrow 2ZnO(s)$$

A
B
C
D
E

2

(3)

[Turn over

Marks KU PS

6. Lemonade can be made by dissolving sugar, lemon and carbon dioxide in water.

A	sugar
B	lemon
C	carbon dioxide
D	water

Identify the solvent used to make lemonade.

| A |
| B |
| C |
| D |

(1)

7. The grid contains the names of some carbohydrates.

A	fructose
B	glucose
C	maltose
D	sucrose
E	starch

(a) Galactose is a monosaccharide found in dairy products.

Identify the **two** isomers of galactose.

A
B
C
D
E

(b) Identify the carbohydrate which is a condensation polymer.

A
B
C
D
E

1

1

(2)

[Turn over

Marks | KU | PS

8. A student made some statements about acids.

A	Acid rain will have no effect on iron structures.
B	A base is a substance which can neutralise an alkali.
C	Treatment of acid indigestion is an example of neutralisation.
D	In a neutralisation reaction the pH of the acid will fall towards 7.
E	When dilute nitric acid reacts with potassium hydroxide solution, the salt potassium nitrate is produced.

Identify the **two** correct statements.

A
B
C
D
E

(2)

Marks KU PS

9. Coffee manufacturers have produced a self-heating can of coffee.

In the centre of the can calcium oxide reacts with water, releasing heat energy.

The equation for the reaction is:

$$CaO(s) + H_2O(\ell) \longrightarrow Ca(OH)_2(aq)$$

A	Calcium oxide is insoluble.
B	The reaction is exothermic.
C	The reaction produces an acidic solution.
D	The temperature of the coffee goes down.
E	0·1 moles of calcium oxide reacts with water producing 0·1 moles of calcium hydroxide.

Identify the **two** correct statements.

A
B
C
D
E

(2)

Marks | KU | PS

PART 2

A total of 40 marks is available in this part of the paper.

10. Hydrogen reacts with other elements to form molecules such as hydrogen fluoride and hydrogen chloride.

(a) Name the family to which fluorine and chlorine belong.

_____

1

(b) The atoms in these molecules are held together by a covalent bond.

Circle the correct words to complete the sentence.

A covalent bond forms when two $\begin{Bmatrix} \text{positive} \\ \text{negative} \\ \text{neutral} \end{Bmatrix}$ nuclei are held together by

their common attraction for a shared pair of $\begin{Bmatrix} \text{protons} \\ \text{neutrons} \\ \text{electrons} \end{Bmatrix}$.

1

(c) The table gives information about some molecules.

Molecule H–X	Size of X/pm	Energy to break bond kJ/mol
H–F	71	569
H–Cl	99	428
H–Br	114	362
H–I	133	295

Describe how the size of element **X** affects the energy needed to break the bond in the molecule.

_____

_____

1

(3)

Marks | KU | PS

11. Crude oil can be transported to a refinery through a steel pipeline.

(a) If the pipeline is not protected the iron will rust.

Name the **ion** formed from water and oxygen, when they accept electrons during rusting.

_____

1

(b) Some parts of the pipeline are under the sea.

What effect would seawater have on the rate of rusting?

_____

_____

1

(c) Magnesium can be attached to the steel pipeline to prevent rusting.

magnesium

What name is given to the **type** of protection provided by the magnesium?

_____

1

(3)

[Turn over

Marks | KU | PS

12. Airbags in cars are designed to prevent injuries in car crashes.

They contain sodium azide (NaN_3) which produces nitrogen gas on impact.

The nitrogen inflates the airbag very quickly.

(*a*) The table gives information on the volume of nitrogen gas produced.

Time/microseconds	Volume of nitrogen gas produced/litres
0	0
5	46
10	64
15	74
20	82
25	88
30	88

(i) Draw a line graph of the results.

Use appropriate scales to fill most of the graph paper.

(Additional graph paper, if required, will be found on page 28.)

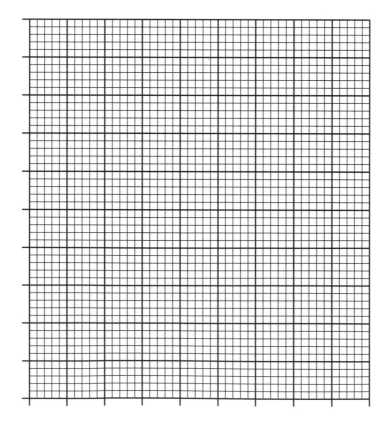

2

(ii) Using your graph, predict the time taken to produce 70 litres of nitrogen gas.

_____ microseconds

1

Marks | KU | PS

12. (continued)

(b) The equation for the production of nitrogen gas is:

$$NaN_3(s) \longrightarrow N_2(g) + Na(s).$$

Balance the equation above.

1

(c) Nitrogen is a non-toxic gas.

Suggest another property of nitrogen which makes it a suitable gas for use in airbags.

_____

_____

1

(5)

[Turn over

Marks KU PS

13. Copper chloride solution can be broken up into its elements by passing electricity through it.

low voltage
d.c.

+   −

carbon
electrodes

copper chloride
solution

(a) Carbon is unreactive and insoluble in water.

Give another reason why it is suitable for use as an electrode.

_____   1

(b) Chlorine gas is released at the positive electrode.

Write an ion-electron equation for the formation of chlorine.
You may wish to use the data booklet to help you.

_____   1

(c) Why do ionic compounds, like copper chloride, conduct electricity when in solution?

_____

_____   1

(3)

Marks KU PS

14. A fizzy drink "Fizz Alive" contains a carbohydrate.

(a) Name all the elements found in a carbohydrate.

_____   1

(b) A student carried out an investigation to find out which carbohydrate was present in "Fizz Alive".

Test 1   **Test 2**

Iodine solution

carbohydrate

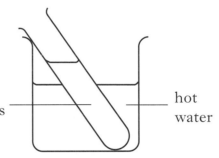

carbohydrate and Benedict's solution

hot water

The results are shown in the table.

Test	Result
Iodine solution	stays brown
Benedict's solution	stays blue

Name the carbohydrate present in "Fizz Alive".

_____   1

(c) A $330\,cm^3$ can of "Fizz Alive" has a carbohydrate concentration of $0.01\,mol/l$.

Calculate the number of moles of carbohydrate in the can of "Fizz Alive".

_____ mol   1

(3)

[Turn over

Marks

15. The diagram represents the structure of an atom.

THE NUCLEUS

Name of Particle	Relative mass
PROTON	(i)
NEUTRON	1

OUTSIDE THE NUCLEUS

Name of Particle	Relative mass
(ii)	0

(*a*) Fill in the missing information for:

(i) _____

(ii) _____   1

15. (continued)

(b) The element uranium has unstable atoms.

These atoms give out radiation and a new element is formed.

$$^{238}_{92}U \longrightarrow {}^{234}_{90}Th + {}^{4}_{2}\alpha$$
radiation

(i) Complete the table to show the number of each type of particle in $^{234}_{90}Th$.

Particle	Number
proton	
neutron	

(ii) Radon is another element which gives out radiation.

$$^{222}_{86}Rn \longrightarrow X + {}^{4}_{2}\alpha$$
radiation

State the **atomic number** of element **X**.

_____

1

1

(3)

[Turn over

16. Anglesite is an ore containing lead(II) sulphate, $PbSO_4$.

(a) Calculate the percentage by mass of lead in anglesite.

_____ %   **2**

(b) Most metals are found combined in the Earth's crust and have to be extracted from their ores.

Place the following metals in the correct space in the table.

lead   aluminium

You may wish to use the data booklet to help you.

Metal	Method of extraction
	electrolysis of molten compound
	using heat and carbon

1

(c) Metal **X** can be extracted from its ore by heat alone.

What does this indicate about the reactivity of **X** compared to both lead and aluminium?

_____

_____   **1**

(d) When a metal is extracted from its ore, metal ions are changed to metal atoms.

Name this **type** of chemical reaction.

_____   **1**

(5)

Marks

17. A student added strips of magnesium to solutions of other metals.

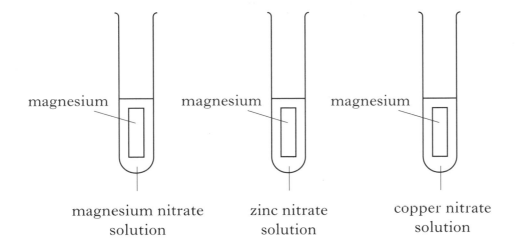

magnesium   magnesium   magnesium

magnesium nitrate solution   zinc nitrate solution   copper nitrate solution

The results are shown in the table.

Solution Metal	magnesium nitrate	zinc nitrate	copper nitrate
magnesium	(i)	(ii)	reaction occurred

(a) In the table, fill in the missing information at (i) and (ii) to show whether or not a chemical reaction has occurred.

You may wish to use the data booklet to help you.   1

(b) The equation for the reaction between magnesium and copper nitrate is:

$$Mg(s) + Cu^{2+}(aq) + 2NO_3^-(aq) \longrightarrow Mg^{2+}(aq) + 2NO_3^-(aq) + Cu(s).$$

(i) Circle the spectator ion in the above equation.   1

(ii) What technique could be used to remove copper from the mixture?

_____

_____   1

(3)

[Turn over

Marks | KU | PS

18. Nitrogen is essential for healthy plant growth.

Nitrogen from the atmosphere can be fixed in a number of ways.

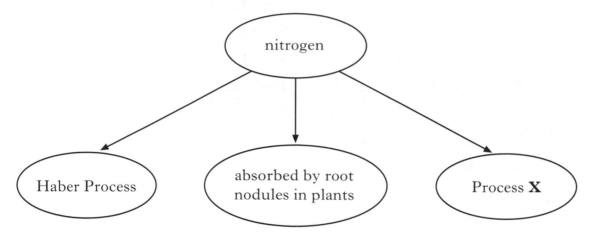

(a) **X** is a natural process which takes place in the atmosphere, producing nitrogen dioxide gas.

What provides the energy for this process?

_____   1

(b) What is present in the root nodules of some plants which convert nitrogen from the atmosphere into nitrogen compounds?

_____

_____   1

(c) The Haber Process is the industrial method of converting nitrogen into a nitrogen compound.

Name the nitrogen compound produced.

_____   1

18. (continued)

(*d*) The nitrogen compound produced in the Haber Process dissolves in water.

The graph shows the solubility of the nitrogen compound at different temperatures.

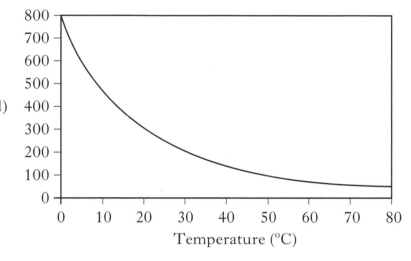

Solubility of nitrogen compound (g/l)

Temperature (°C)

Write a general statement describing the effect of temperature on the solubility of the nitrogen compound.

_____

_____

1

(4)

[Turn over

Marks | KU | PS

19. The octane number indicates how efficiently a fuel burns.

Alkane	Molecular Formula	Full Structural Formula	Octane Number
2-methylbutane	C_5H_{12}	(structure shown)	93
2-methylpentane	C_6H_{14}	(structure shown)	71
2-methylhexane	C_7H_{16}		47
2-methylheptane	C_8H_{18}	(structure shown)	2
2-methyloctane	C_9H_{20}	(structure shown)	2

(*a*) Draw the **full** structural formula for 2-methylhexane.

1

Marks | KU | PS

19. (continued)

(b) 2-methylpentane and hexane have the same molecular formula (C_6H_{14}), but different structural formulae.

What term is used to describe this pair of alkanes?

_____

1

(c) Using information in the table, predict the octane number for 2-methylheptane.

_____

1

(3)

[Turn over

20. Molten iron is used to join steel railway lines together.

Molten iron is produced when aluminium reacts with iron oxide.

The equation for the reaction is:

$$2Al + Fe_2O_3 \longrightarrow 2Fe + Al_2O_3$$

(a) Calculate the mass of iron produced from 40 grams of iron oxide.

_____ g   **2**

(b) The formula for iron oxide is Fe_2O_3.

What is the charge on this iron ion?

_____   **1**

Marks | KU | PS

20. (continued)

(c) Iron can also be produced from iron ore, Fe_2O_3, in a blast furnace.

iron ore, carbon and limestone

1000 °C

1500 °C

2000 °C

air

air

molten iron

The main reactions taking place are:

$$C(s) + O_2(g) \longrightarrow CO_2(g)$$

$$CO_2(g) + C(s) \longrightarrow 2CO(g)$$

$$Fe_2O_3(s) + 3CO(g) \longrightarrow 2Fe(\ell) + 3CO_2(g)$$

(i) When air is blown into the furnace the temperature rises.

Suggest another reason why **air** is blown into the furnace.

_____

_____

1

(ii) Explain why the temperature at the bottom of the blast furnace should **not** drop below 1535 °C.

You may wish to use the data booklet to help you.

_____

_____

1

(5)

[END OF QUESTION PAPER]

ADDITIONAL SPACE FOR ANSWERS

ADDITIONAL GRAPH PAPER FOR QUESTION 12(*a*)(i)

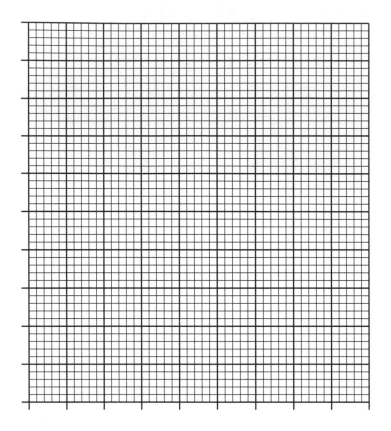

STANDARD GRADE | CREDIT

2009

[BLANK PAGE]

C

FOR OFFICIAL USE

	KU	PS
Total Marks		

0500/402

NATIONAL
QUALIFICATIONS
2009

MONDAY, 11 MAY
10.50 AM – 12.20 PM

CHEMISTRY
STANDARD GRADE
Credit Level

Fill in these boxes and read what is printed below.

Full name of centre

Town

Forename(s)

Surname

Date of birth

Day Month Year   Scottish candidate number   Number of seat

1 All questions should be attempted.

2 Necessary data will be found in the Data Booklet provided for Chemistry at Standard Grade and Intermediate 2.

3 The questions may be answered in any order but all answers are to be written in this answer book, and must be written clearly and legibly in ink.

4 Rough work, if any should be necessary, as well as the fair copy, is to be written in this book.

Rough work should be scored through when the fair copy has been written.

5 Additional space for answers and rough work will be found at the end of the book.

6 The size of the space provided for an answer should not be taken as an indication of how much to write. It is not necessary to use all the space.

7 Before leaving the examination room you must give this book to the invigilator. If you do not, you may lose all the marks for this paper.

PART 1

In Questions 1 to 8 of this part of the paper, an answer is given by circling the appropriate letter (or letters) in the answer grid provided.

In some questions, two letters are required for full marks.

If more than the correct number of answers is given, marks will be deducted.

A total of 20 marks is available in this part of the paper.

SAMPLE QUESTION

A		B		C	
	CH_4		H_2		CO_2
D		E		F	
	CO		C_2H_5OH		C

(a) Identify the hydrocarbon.

Ⓐ	B	C
D	E	F

The one correct answer to part (a) is A. This should be circled.

(b) Identify the **two** elements.

A	Ⓑ	C
D	E	Ⓕ

As indicated in this question, there are **two** correct answers to part (b). These are B and F. Both answers are circled.

If, after you have recorded your answer, you decide that you have made an error and wish to make a change, you should cancel the original answer and circle the answer you now consider to be correct. Thus, in part (a), if you want to change an answer A to an answer D, your answer sheet would look like this:

Ⱥ	B	C
Ⓓ	E	F

If you want to change back to an answer which has already been scored out, you should enter a tick (✓) in the box of the answer of your choice, thus:

✓Ⱥ	B	C
Ⱦ	E	F

Marks | KU | PS

1. Many solutions are used for chemical tests.

A	B	C
Benedict's reagent	lime water	bromine solution
D	E	F
pH indicator	iodine solution	ferroxyl indicator

(a) Identify the solution which could be used to test for maltose.

A	B	C
D	E	F

1

(b) Identify the solution which is used to test for $Fe^{2+}(aq)$.

A	B	C
D	E	F

1

(2)

[Turn over

Marks | KU | PS

2. Many chemical compounds contain ions.

A	B	C
strontium chloride	lithium oxide	calcium oxide
D	E	F
barium fluoride	sodium fluoride	potassium chloride

(a) Identify the compound which produces a green flame colour.

You may wish to use the data booklet to help you.

A	B	C
D	E	F

1

(b) Identify the compound in which **both** ions have the same electron arrangement as argon.

A	B	C
D	E	F

1

(2)

3. The table contains information about some substances.

Substance	Melting point/°C	Boiling point/°C	Conducts as	
			a solid	a liquid
A	639	3228	yes	yes
B	2967	3273	no	no
C	159	211	no	no
D	1402	2497	no	yes
E	27	677	yes	yes

(a) Identify the substance which exists as a covalent network.

A
B
C
D
E

(b) Identify the substance which could be calcium fluoride.

A
B
C
D
E

[Turn over

Marks | KU | PS

4. The grid shows the names of some ionic compounds.

A	B	C
aluminium bromide	sodium chloride	potassium hydroxide
D	E	F
sodium sulphate	potassium bromide	calcium chloride

(a) Identify the base.

A	B	C
D	E	F

1

(b) Identify the **two** compounds whose solutions would form a precipitate when mixed.

You may wish to use the data booklet to help you.

A	B	C
D	E	F

1

(c) Identify the compound with a formula of the type **XY₂**, where **X** is a metal.

A	B	C
D	E	F

1

(3)

Marks | KU | PS

5. The names of some hydrocarbons are shown in the grid.

A ethane	B pentene	C cyclohexane
D pentane	E cyclopentane	F propene

(a) Identify the **two** isomers.

A	B	C
D	E	F

1

(b) Identify the hydrocarbon with the highest boiling point.

You may wish to use the data booklet to help you.

A	B	C
D	E	F

1

(c) Identify the **two** hydrocarbons which can take part in an addition reaction with hydrogen.

A	B	C
D	E	F

1

(3)

[Turn over

Marks | KU | PS

6. Reactions can be represented using chemical equations.

A	$Fe^{2+}(aq) + 2e^- \rightarrow Fe(s)$
B	$Fe^{2+}(aq) \rightarrow Fe^{3+}(aq) + e^-$
C	$2H_2(g) + O_2(g) \rightarrow 2H_2O(g)$
D	$2H_2O(\ell) + O_2(g) + 4e^- \rightarrow 4OH^-(aq)$
E	$SO_2(g) + H_2O(\ell) \rightarrow 2H^+(aq) + SO_3^{2-}(aq)$

(a) Identify the equation which shows the formation of acid rain.

A
B
C
D
E

1

(b) Identify the equation which represents a combustion reaction.

A
B
C
D
E

1

(c) Identify the **two** equations which are involved in the corrosion of iron.

A
B
C
D
E

2

(4)

7. The grid contains information about the particles found in atoms.

A	B	C
relative mass = 1	charge = zero	relative mass almost zero
D	E	F
charge = 1–	found outside the nucleus	charge = 1+

Identify the **two** terms which can be applied to protons.

A	B	C
D	E	F

(2)

[Turn over

Marks | KU | PS

8. The fractional distillation of crude oil was demonstrated to a class.

Six fractions were numbered in the order they were collected.

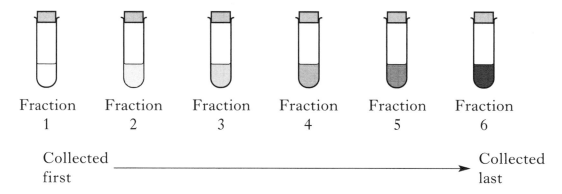

| Fraction 1 | Fraction 2 | Fraction 3 | Fraction 4 | Fraction 5 | Fraction 6 |

Collected first ——————————————→ Collected last

Identify the **two** correct statements.

A	Fraction 6 evaporates most easily.
B	Fraction 5 is less viscous than fraction 4.
C	Fraction 2 is more flammable than fraction 3.
D	Fraction 1 has a lower boiling range than fraction 2.
E	The molecules in fraction 3 are larger than those in fraction 4.

A
B
C
D
E

(2)

[Turn over for Part 2 on *Page twelve*

Marks   KU   PS

PART 2

A total of 40 marks is available in this part of the paper.

9. There are three different types of neon atom.

Type of atom	Number of protons	Number of neutrons
$^{20}_{10}Ne$		
$^{21}_{10}Ne$		
$^{22}_{10}Ne$		

(a) Complete the table to show the number of protons and neutrons in each type of neon atom.

         1

(b) What term is used to describe these different types of neon atom?

_____

         1

(c) A natural sample of neon has an average atomic mass of 20·2.

What is the mass number of the most common type of atom in the sample of neon?

_____

         1

         (3)

Marks | KU | PS

10. Aluminium metal can be produced by passing electricity through molten aluminium oxide.

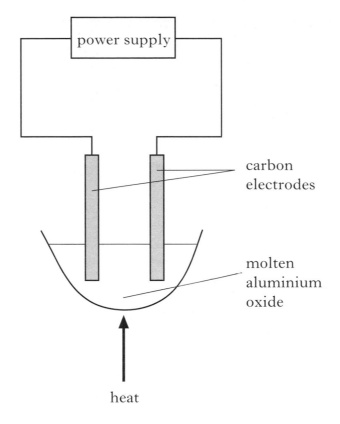

power supply

carbon electrodes

molten aluminium oxide

heat

(a) Name this process.

_____ 1

(b) Write the ionic formula for aluminium oxide.

1

(c) Why do ionic compounds, like aluminium oxide, conduct electricity when molten?

_____

_____ 1

(3)

[Turn over

Marks | KU | PS

11. A student burned gas **X** and the products were passed through the apparatus shown.

gas **X** →

ice

to water pump

lime water

test tube **A**   test tube **B**

(a) The results are shown in the table.

Observation in test tube A	Observation in test tube B
colourless liquid forms	lime water turns milky

Using the information in the table, name two **elements** which **must** be present in gas **X**.

_____

1

(b) The experiment was repeated using hydrogen gas.

Complete the table showing the results which would have been obtained.

Observation in test tube A	Observation in test tube B

1

(2)

12. Hydrogen can form bonds with other elements.

The diagram shows the arrangement of outer electrons in a molecule of hydrogen chloride.

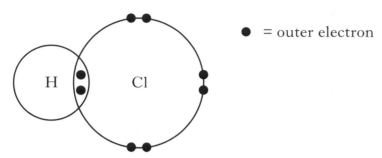

● = outer electron

(a) What type of bonding is present in a hydrogen chloride molecule?

_____   1

(b) Draw a similar diagram, showing **all** outer electrons, to represent a molecule of phosphine, PH_3.

1

(2)

[Turn over

Marks | KU | PS

13. The apparatus below was used to investigate the reaction between lumps of calcium carbonate and dilute hydrochloric acid.

Excess acid was used to make sure all the calcium carbonate reacted.

A balance was used to measure the mass lost during the reaction.

dilute hydrochloric acid   calcium carbonate

balance

(a) Name the type of chemical reaction taking place when calcium carbonate reacts with dilute hydrochloric acid.

_____ 1

(b) The results are shown in the table.

Time/minutes	0	0·5	1·0	2·0	3·0	4·0	5·0
Mass lost/g	0	0·36	0·52	0·70	0·80	0·86	0·86

(i) Why is mass lost during the reaction?

_____

_____ 1

13. **(b)** **(continued)**

(ii) Draw a line graph of the results.

Use appropriate scales to fill most of the graph paper.

(Additional graph paper, if required, will be found on page 26.)

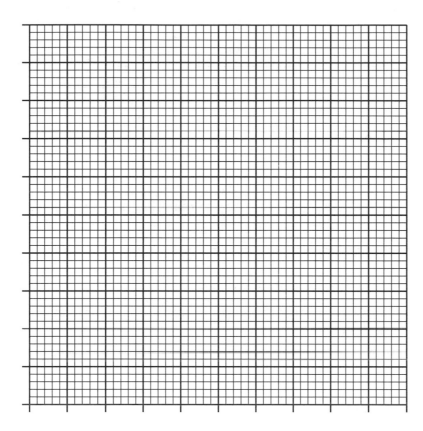

2

(c) The experiment was repeated using the same volume and concentration of acid. The same mass of calcium carbonate was used but **powder** instead of lumps.

Suggest how much mass would have been lost after three minutes.

_____ g   **1**

(5)

[Turn over

Marks KU PS

14. (*a*) The flow diagram shows how ammonia is converted to nitric acid.

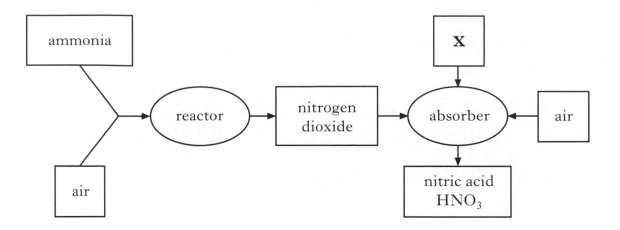

(i) Name the industrial process used to manufacture nitric acid.

_____ 1

(ii) The reactor contains a platinum catalyst.

Why is it **not** necessary to continue heating the catalyst once the reaction has started?

_____

_____ 1

(iii) Name substance **X**.

_____ 1

(*b*) Ammonia and nitric acid react together to form ammonium nitrate, NH_4NO_3.

Calculate the percentage by mass of nitrogen in ammonium nitrate.

Show your working clearly.

_____% 2

(5)

Marks | KU | PS

15. A student carried out some experiments with four metals and their oxides. The results are shown in the table.

Metal	Reaction with cold water	Reaction with dilute acid	Effect of heat on metal oxide
W	no reaction	no reaction	no reaction
X	no reaction	gas produced	no reaction
Y	gas produced	gas produced	no reaction
Z	no reaction	no reaction	metal produced

(a) Place the four metals in order of reactivity (**most reactive first**).

_____   1

(b) Name the gas produced when metal **Y** reacts with cold water.

_____   1

(c) Suggest names for metals **Y** and **Z**.

metal **Y** _____   metal **Z** _____   1

(3)

[Turn over

Marks | KU | PS

16. The diagram shows the main stages in the making of malt whisky.

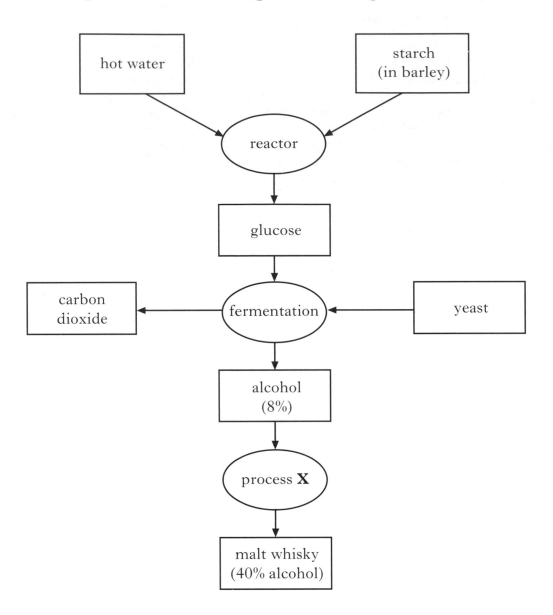

(a) Name the type of chemical reaction which takes place in the reactor.

_____   1

Marks   KU   PS

16.   **(continued)**

(b)   The equation for the reaction taking place during fermentation is:

$$C_6H_{12}O_6 \longrightarrow C_2H_5OH + CO_2$$

Balance this equation.   1

(c)   What name is given to process **X**?

_____   1

(d)   Ethanol, C_2H_5OH, is the alcohol found in whisky.

A bottle of whisky contains 230 g of ethanol.

Calculate the number of moles of ethanol present in the whisky.

Show your working clearly.

_____ mol   2

(5)

[Turn over

Marks | KU | PS

17. A student set up the cell shown.

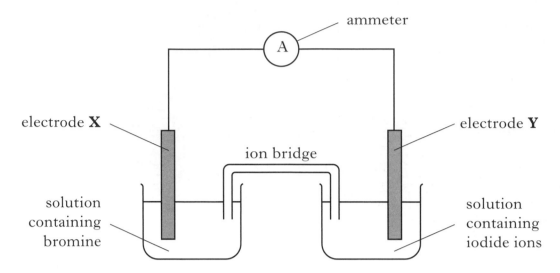

The reaction taking place at electrode **Y** is:

$$2I^-(aq) \longrightarrow I_2(s) + 2e^-$$

(a) Name the type of chemical reaction taking place at electrode **Y**.

_____ 1

(b) **On the diagram**, clearly mark the path and direction of the electron flow. 1

(c) Describe a test, including the result, which would show that iodine had formed at electrode **Y**.

_____

_____ 1

(d) Write the ion-electron equation for the chemical reaction taking place at electrode **X**.

1

(4)

Marks | KU | PS

18. When superglue sets, a polymer is formed.

Part of the polymer structure is shown.

(a) Draw the structure of the repeating unit in the superglue polymer.

1

(b) The polymer shown above contains methyl groups (CH_3).

Another type of superglue, used to close cuts, has the methyl groups replaced by either butyl groups (C_4H_9) or octyl groups.

Complete the table to show the number of carbon and hydrogen atoms in an octyl group.

	Number of atoms	
Group	Carbon	Hydrogen
methyl	1	3
butyl	4	9
octyl		

1

(c) Name a toxic gas given off when superglue burns.

_____

1

(3)

[Turn over

Marks | KU | PS

19. (*a*) The table gives information about some members of the alkane family.

Name	Molecular formula	Boiling point/°C
nonane	C_9H_{20}	151
decane	$C_{10}H_{22}$	174
undecane	$C_{11}H_{24}$	196
dodecane	$C_{12}H_{26}$	

Predict the boiling point of dodecane.

_____°C   1

(*b*) What term is used to describe any family of compounds, like the alkanes, which have the same general formula and similar chemical properties?

_____   1

(*c*) The equation for the burning of nonane is:

$$C_9H_{20} + 14O_2 \longrightarrow 9CO_2 + 10H_2O$$

Calculate the mass of water produced when 6·4 grams of nonane is burned.

Show your working clearly.

 g   2

Marks | KU | PS

19. (continued)

(d) Alkanes can be prepared by the Kolbé synthesis.

ethanoate ions   ethane

Draw a structural formula for the alkane produced when propanoate ions are used instead of ethanoate ions.

1

(5)

[END OF QUESTION PAPER]

CREDIT CHEMISTRY 2009   90   OFFICIAL SQA PAST PAPERS

DO NOT
WRITE IN
THIS
MARGIN

KU | PS

ADDITIONAL SPACE FOR ANSWERS

ADDITIONAL GRAPH PAPER FOR QUESTION 13(b)(ii)

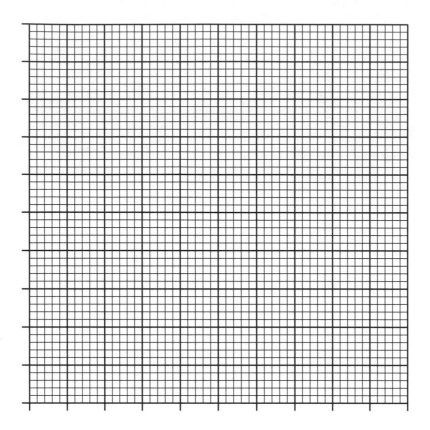

OFFICIAL SQA PAST PAPERS   CREDIT CHEMISTRY 2009

DO NOT
WRITE IN
THIS
MARGIN

KU PS

ADDITIONAL SPACE FOR ANSWERS

ADDITIONAL SPACE FOR ANSWERS

STANDARD GRADE | CREDIT

2010

[BLANK PAGE]

FOR OFFICIAL USE

C

KU   PS

Total Marks

0500/402

NATIONAL QUALIFICATIONS 2010

FRIDAY, 30 APRIL 10.50 AM – 12.20 PM

CHEMISTRY STANDARD GRADE Credit Level

Fill in these boxes and read what is printed below.

Full name of centre

Town

Forename

Surname

Date of birth

| Day | Month | Year | Scottish candidate number | Number of seat |

1 All questions should be attempted.

2 Necessary data will be found in the Data Booklet provided for Chemistry at Standard Grade and Intermediate 2.

3 The questions may be answered in any order but all answers are to be written in this answer book, and must be written clearly and legibly in ink.

4 Rough work, if any should be necessary, as well as the fair copy, is to be written in this book.

   Rough work should be scored through when the fair copy has been written.

5 Additional space for answers and rough work will be found at the end of the book.

6 The size of the space provided for an answer should not be taken as an indication of how much to write.   It is not necessary to use all the space.

7 Before leaving the examination room you must give this book to the Invigilator. If you do not, you may lose all the marks for this paper.

PART 1

In Questions 1 to 9 of this part of the paper, an answer is given by circling the appropriate letter (or letters) in the answer grid provided.

In some questions, two letters are required for full marks.

If more than the correct number of answers is given, marks will be deducted.

A total of 20 marks is available in this part of the paper.

SAMPLE QUESTION

A		B		C	
	CH_4		H_2		CO_2
D		E		F	
	CO		C_2H_5OH		C

(a) Identify the hydrocarbon.

Ⓐ	B	C
D	E	F

The one correct answer to part (a) is A. This should be circled.

(b) Identify the **two** elements.

A	Ⓑ	C
D	E	Ⓕ

As indicated in this question, there are **two** correct answers to part (b). These are B and F. Both answers are circled.

If, after you have recorded your answer, you decide that you have made an error and wish to make a change, you should cancel the original answer and circle the answer you now consider to be correct. Thus, in part (a), if you want to change an answer A to an answer D, your answer sheet would look like this:

A̶	B	C
Ⓓ	E	F

If you want to change back to an answer which has already been scored out, you should enter a tick (✓) in the box of the answer of your choice, thus:

✓A̶	B	C
D̶	E	F

1. Crude oil can be separated into fractions.

Fraction	Number of carbon atoms per molecule
A	1–4
B	4–10
C	10–16
D	16–20
E	20+

crude oil ⟶

(a) Identify the fraction which is the most viscous.

A
B
C
D
E

1

(b) Identify the fraction used as camping gas.

A
B
C
D
E

1

(2)

[Turn over

2. The grid contains the symbols for some common elements.

A		B		C	
H		N		Si	
D		E		F	
Al		Mg		O	

(a) Identify the element which has a density of $1.74\,g/cm^3$.

You may wish to use the data booklet to help you.

A	B	C
D	E	F

1

(b) Identify the **two** elements which react together to form a molecule with the same shape as a methane molecule.

A	B	C
D	E	F

1

(c) Identify the **two** elements which form an ionic compound with a formula of type X_2Y_3, where **X** is a metal.

A	B	C
D	E	F

1

(3)

3. The grid shows information about some particles.

A	B	C
$^{23}_{11}Na$	$^{18}_{8}O$	$^{40}_{19}K^+$
D	E	F
$^{24}_{12}Mg^{2+}$	$^{35}_{17}Cl^-$	$^{16}_{8}O$

(a) Identify the **two** particles with the same number of neutrons.

A	B	C
D	E	F

1

(b) Identify the particle which has the same electron arrangement as neon.

A	B	C
D	E	F

1

(2)

[Turn over

4. The grid shows the names of some carbohydrates.

A	fructose
B	glucose
C	maltose
D	sucrose
E	starch

(a) Identify the condensation polymer.

A
B
C
D
E

1

(b) Identify the **two** monosaccharides.

A
B
C
D
E

1

(2)

Marks | KU | PS

5. Iron can be coated with different materials which provide a physical barrier against corrosion.

A	oil
B	zinc
C	plastic
D	tin
E	paint

(a) Identify the coating which is used to galvanise iron.

| A |
| B |
| C |
| D |
| E |

1

(b) Identify the coating which, if scratched, would cause the iron to rust faster than normal.

| A |
| B |
| C |
| D |
| E |

1

(2)

[Turn over

Marks | KU | PS

6. The structures of some hydrocarbons are shown in the grid.

(a) Identify the **two** hydrocarbons with the general formula C_nH_{2n}, which do **not** react quickly with bromine solution.

A	B	C
D	E	F

1

(b) Identify the hydrocarbon which is the first member of a homologous series.

A	B	C
D	E	F

1

(c) Identify the **two** isomers of

A	B	C
D	E	F

1

(3)

7. Elements can be used in different ways.

A	B	C
chlorine	potassium	platinum

D	E	F
hydrogen	neon	iron

(a) Identify the element which is a reactant in the Haber Process.

A	B	C
D	E	F

1

(b) Identify the element used as the catalyst in the manufacture of nitric acid (Ostwald Process).

A	B	C
D	E	F

1

(2)

[Turn over

Marks

8. The grid shows some statements which can be applied to different solutions.

A	It has a pH less than 7.
B	It conducts electricity.
C	It contains less $OH^-(aq)$ ions than pure water.
D	It does not neutralise dilute hydrochloric acid.
E	When diluted the concentration of $OH^-(aq)$ ions decreases.

Identify the **two** statements which are correct for an alkaline solution.

A
B
C
D
E

(2)

Marks

9. The grid shows pairs of chemicals.

A	B	C
copper carbonate + dilute sulphuric acid	lead nitrate solution + potassium iodide solution	potassium hydroxide + nitric acid
D	E	F
copper + water	silver + hydrochloric acid	ammonium nitrate + sodium hydroxide

Which **two** boxes contain a pair of chemicals that react together to form a gas?

A	B	C
D	E	F

(2)

[Turn over

Marks

PART 2

A total of 40 marks is available in this part of the paper.

10. Poly(methyl methacrylate) is a synthetic polymer used to manufacture perspex.

    (a) What is meant by the term **synthetic**?

    _____   1

    (b) The structure of the methyl methacrylate monomer is shown.

$$
\begin{array}{ccc}
H & & CH_3 \\
| & & | \\
C & = & C \\
| & & | \\
H & & COOCH_3
\end{array}
$$

    methyl methacrylate

    (i) Draw a section of the poly(methyl methacrylate) polymer, showing three monomer units joined together.

    1

    (ii) Name the type of polymerisation taking place.

    _____   1

    (c) Name a toxic gas produced when poly(methyl methacrylate) burns.

    _____   1

    (4)

Marks   KU | PS

11. A student set up an experiment to investigate the breakdown of glucose to form alcohol.

At the start a deflated balloon was attached to the top of the tube.

After two hours the balloon inflates as shown.

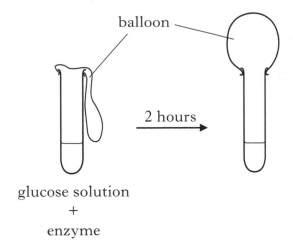

balloon

2 hours

glucose solution
+
enzyme

(a) (i)   Name the type of chemical reaction taking place in the test tube.

_____   1

(ii)   Name the gas produced, which causes the balloon to inflate.

_____   1

(b) The student repeated the experiment at 80 °C.

What effect would this have on how much the balloon inflates?

_____

_____

_____   1

(3)

[Turn over

Marks | KU | PS

12. A student added magnesium ribbon to an excess of dilute sulphuric acid and measured the volume of hydrogen gas produced.

The reaction stopped when all the magnesium was used up.

magnesium ribbon   dilute sulphuric acid

The results are shown in the table.

Time/s	0	10	20	40	50	60	70
Volume of hydrogen gas/cm^3	0	20	32	50	52	53	53

(*a*) State the test for hydrogen gas.

_____

_____ 1

(*b*) Draw a line graph of the results.

Use appropriate scales to fill most of the graph paper.

(Additional graph paper, if required, will be found on page 24.)

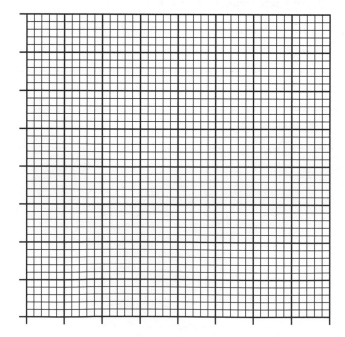

2

Marks

DO NOT WRITE IN THIS MARGIN

KU | PS

12. (continued)

(c) Using your graph, predict the volume of hydrogen gas produced during the first 30 seconds.

_____ cm^3 **1**

(d) The student repeated the experiment using a higher concentration of acid. The same volume of acid and the same mass of magnesium ribbon were used.

What volume of hydrogen gas would have been produced after 60 seconds?

_____ cm^3 **1**

(e) Calculate the mass of hydrogen produced when 4·9 g of magnesium reacts with an excess of dilute sulphuric acid.

$$Mg + H_2SO_4 \longrightarrow MgSO_4 + H_2$$

_____ g   **2**

(7)

[Turn over

Marks | KU | PS

13. A student set up the following experiment to investigate the colour of ions in nickel(II) chromate solution.

d.c. supply

electrode **A**

electrode **B**

colourless
electrolyte

nickel(II) chromate
solution

The results are shown.

Green colour moves towards electrode **A**
Yellow colour moves towards electrode **B**

(a) Why **must** a d.c. supply be used?

_____

_____

_____   **1**

(b) State the colour of the nickel(II) ions.

_____   **1**

(c) Write the **ionic** formula for nickel(II) chromate.

1

(3)

DO NOT
WRITE IN
THIS
MARGIN

Marks   KU   PS

14. The Eurofighter "Typhoon" is made from many newly developed materials including titanium alloys.

(a) The first step in extracting titanium from its ore is to convert it into titanium(IV) chloride.

Titanium(IV) chloride is a liquid at room temperature and does **not** conduct electricity.

What type of bonding, does this suggest, is present in titanium(IV) chloride?

_____   1

(b) Titanium(IV) chloride is then reduced to titanium metal.

The equation for the reaction taking place is:

$$TiCl_4 \quad + \quad Na \quad \longrightarrow \quad Ti \quad + \quad NaCl$$

(i) Balance the equation.   1

(ii) What does this reaction suggest about the reactivity of titanium compared to that of sodium?

_____   1

(3)

[Turn over

Marks KU | PS

15. Scuba divers can suffer from painful and potentially fatal problems if they rise to the surface of the water too quickly. This causes dissolved nitrogen in their blood to form bubbles of nitrogen gas.

Distance from surface of water/m	Concentration of dissolved nitrogen/units
0	11·5
10	23·0
20	34·5
30	46·0
40	57·5

(a) Describe the relationship between the distance from the surface of the water and the concentration of dissolved nitrogen.

_____

_____

_____   **1**

(b) Predict the concentration of dissolved nitrogen at 60 m.

_____ units   **1**

(c) A nitrogen molecule is held together by three covalent bonds.

Circle the correct words to complete the sentence.

In a covalent bond the atoms are held together by the attraction

between the positive $\begin{Bmatrix} \text{electrons} \\ \text{neutrons} \\ \text{protons} \end{Bmatrix}$ and the shared pair of negative

$\begin{Bmatrix} \text{electrons} \\ \text{neutrons} \\ \text{protons} \end{Bmatrix}$.   **1**

(3)

DO NOT WRITE IN THIS MARGIN

Marks | KU | PS

16. (a) Galena is an ore containing lead sulphide, PbS.

(i) What is the charge on this lead ion?

_____

1

(ii) Calculate the percentage by mass of lead in galena, PbS.

_____ % 2

(b) Most metals have to be extracted from their ores.

(i) Name the metal extracted in a Blast furnace.

_____

1

(ii) Place the following metals in the correct space in the table.

copper, mercury, aluminium

You may wish to use the data booklet to help you.

Metal	Method of extraction
	using heat alone
	electrolysis of molten ore
	heating with carbon

1

(5)

[Turn over

Marks

17. Iron displaces silver from silver(I) nitrate solution.

The equation for the reaction is:

$$Fe(s) + 2Ag^+(aq) + 2NO_3^-(aq) \longrightarrow Fe^{2+}(aq) + 2Ag(s) + 2NO_3^-(aq)$$

(a) Circle the spectator ion in the above equation.   1

(b) Describe a chemical test, including the result, to show that $Fe^{2+}(aq)$ ions are formed.

_____

_____   1

(c) Write the ion-electron equation for the **reduction** step in the reaction.

You may wish to use the data book to help you.

1

(d) This reaction can also be carried out in a cell.

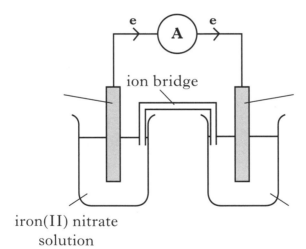

iron(II) nitrate
    solution

Complete the three labels on the diagram.   1

(An additional diagram, if required, will be found on page 24.)   **(4)**

18. Ethers are useful chemicals.

Some are listed in the table.

Structural formula	Name of ether
$CH_3CH_2 - O - CH_2CH_3$	ethoxyethane
$CH_3 - O - CH_2CH_2CH_3$	methoxypropane
$CH_3 - O - CH_2CH_3$	methoxyethane
$CH_3CH_2 - O - CH_2CH_2CH_3$	**X**

(a) Suggest a name for ether **X**.

_____

1

(b) The boiling points of ethers and alkanes are approximately the same when they have a **similar** relative formula mass.

Suggest the **boiling point** of ethoxyethane (relative formula mass 74).

You may wish to use the data booklet to help you.

_____ °C   1

(2)

[Turn over

Marks | KU | PS

19. A student carried out a titration using the chemicals and apparatus below.

hydrochloric acid
0·1 mol/l

	Rough titre	1st titre	2nd titre
Initial burette reading/cm^3	0·3	0·2	0·5
Final burette reading/cm^3	26·6	25·3	25·4
Volume used/cm^3	26·3	25·1	24·9

10 cm^3
sodium hydroxide
solution + indicator

(a) Using the results in the table, calculate the **average** volume of hydrochloric acid required to neutralise the sodium hydroxide solution.

_____ cm^3 **1**

(b) The equation for the reaction is:

$$HCl \ + \ NaOH \longrightarrow H_2O \ + \ NaCl$$

Using your answer from part (a), calculate the concentration of the sodium hydroxide solution.

Show your working clearly.

_____ mol/l   **2**

(3)

Marks KU PS

20. Chemists have discovered a way to insert a –CH$_2$– group into any bond which includes an atom of hydrogen.

When a –CH$_2$– group is inserted into a methanol molecule the following reaction takes place.

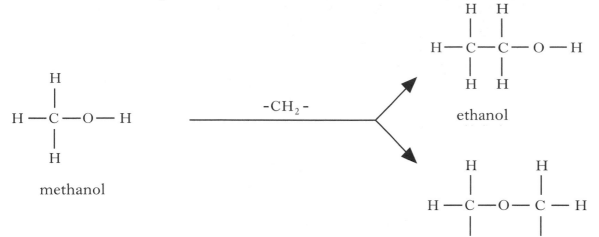

methanol

ethanol

(a) This reaction can be repeated using ethanol.

One of the products for this reaction is shown.

ethanol

molecule **X**

(i) Suggest a name for molecule **X**.

_____   1

(ii) Draw a structural formula for another molecule which would be formed in this reaction.

1

(b) Identify the **two** products formed when molecule **X** is completely burned in a plentiful supply of oxygen.

_____   1

(3)

[END OF QUESTION PAPER]

ADDITIONAL SPACE FOR ANSWERS

ADDITIONAL GRAPH PAPER FOR QUESTION 12(*b*)

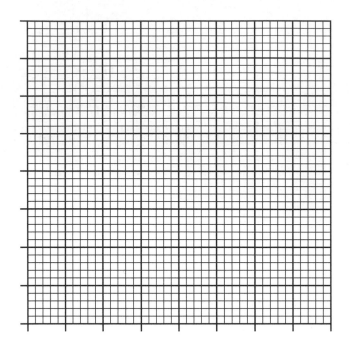

ADDITIONAL DIAGRAM FOR QUESTION 17(*d*)

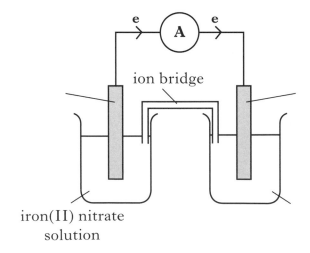

iron(II) nitrate
solution

[BLANK PAGE]

C

FOR OFFICIAL USE

Total Marks	KU · PS

0500/402

NATIONAL
QUALIFICATIONS
2011

THURSDAY, 26 MAY
10.50 AM – 12.20 PM

CHEMISTRY
STANDARD GRADE
Credit Level

Fill in these boxes and read what is printed below.

Full name of centre

Town

Forename(s)

Surname

Date of birth

Day   Month   Year   Scottish candidate number   Number of seat

1 All questions should be attempted.

2 Necessary data will be found in the Data Booklet provided for Chemistry at Standard Grade and Intermediate 2.

3 The questions may be answered in any order but all answers are to be written in this answer book, and must be written clearly and legibly in ink.

4 Rough work, if any should be necessary, as well as the fair copy, is to be written in this book.

   Rough work should be scored through when the fair copy has been written.

5 Additional space for answers and rough work will be found at the end of the book.

6 The size of the space provided for an answer should not be taken as an indication of how much to write. It is not necessary to use all the space.

7 Before leaving the examination room you must give this book to the Invigilator. If you do not, you may lose all the marks for this paper.

PART 1

In Questions 1 to 10 of this part of the paper, an answer is given by circling the appropriate letter (or letters) in the answer grid provided.

In some questions, two letters are required for full marks.

If more than the correct number of answers is given, marks will be deducted.

A total of 20 marks is available in this part of the paper.

SAMPLE QUESTION

A	CH$_4$	B	H$_2$	C	CO$_2$
D	CO	E	C$_2$H$_5$OH	F	C

(a) Identify the hydrocarbon.

Ⓐ	B	C
D	E	F

The one correct answer to part (a) is A. This should be circled.

(b) Identify the **two** elements.

A	Ⓑ	C
D	E	Ⓕ

As indicated in this question, there are **two** correct answers to part (b). These are B and F. Both answers are circled.

If, after you have recorded your answer, you decide that you have made an error and wish to make a change, you should cancel the original answer and circle the answer you now consider to be correct. Thus, in part (a), if you want to change an answer A to an answer D, your answer sheet would look like this:

A̸	B	C
Ⓓ	E	F

If you want to change back to an answer which has already been scored out, you should enter a tick (✓) in the box of the answer of your choice, thus:

✓A̸	B	C
D̸	E	F

Marks | KU | PS

1. Limewater can be made by dissolving calcium hydroxide in water.

   Identify the term used to describe the water.

A	solute
B	solvent
C	solution
D	insoluble

A
B
C
D

(1)

[Turn over

2. Distillation of crude oil produces several fractions.

Fraction	Number of carbon atoms per molecule
A	1–4
B	4–10
C	10–16
D	16–20
E	20+

crude oil ⟶

(a) Identify the fraction which is used to tar roads.

A
B
C
D
E

1

(b) Identify the fraction which is most flammable.

A
B
C
D
E

1

(2)

Marks | KU | PS

3. The grid shows the symbols of some elements.

A O	B K	C P
D F	E Li	F Al

(a) Identify the element with the lowest density.

You may wish to use the data booklet to help you.

A	B	C
D	E	F

1

(b) Identify the **two** elements which can form ions with the same electron arrangement as argon.

You may wish to use the data booklet to help you.

A	B	C
D	E	F

1

(c) Identify the **two** elements which would react together to form a molecule with the same shape as an ammonia molecule.

A	B	C
D	E	F

1

(3)

[Turn over

4. The table contains information about some substances.

Substance	Melting point/°C	Boiling point/°C	Conducts as a solid	Conducts as a liquid
A	−7	59	no	no
B	1492	2897	yes	yes
C	1407	2357	no	no
D	606	1305	no	yes
E	−39	357	yes	yes
F	−78	−33	no	no

(a) Identify the substance which is a gas at 0 °C.

A
B
C
D
E
F

(b) Identify the **two** substances which exist as molecules.

A
B
C
D
E
F

5. The grid shows the formulae of some oxides.

A	B	C
ZnO	NO_2	K_2O
D	E	F
CuO	Fe_2O_3	CO

(a) Identify the **two** oxides which are covalent.

A	B	C
D	E	F

1

(b) Identify the oxide which dissolves in water to give an alkaline solution.

You may wish to use the data booklet to help you.

A	B	C
D	E	F

1

(c) Identify the oxide which is reduced in a blast furnace.

A	B	C
D	E	F

1

(3)

[Turn over

6. Equations are used to represent chemical reactions.

A	$2H_2(g) + O_2(g) \longrightarrow 2H_2O(\ell)$
B	$2H_2O(\ell) + O_2(g) + 4e^- \longrightarrow 4OH^-(aq)$
C	$CH_4(g) + 2O_2(g) \longrightarrow CO_2(g) + 2H_2O(\ell)$
D	$H^+(aq) + OH^-(aq) \longrightarrow H_2O(\ell)$
E	$Zn(s) + FeSO_4(aq) \longrightarrow Fe(s) + ZnSO_4(aq)$

(a) Identify the equation which represents neutralisation.

A
B
C
D
E

1

(b) Identify the equation involved in the rusting of iron.

A
B
C
D
E

1

(2)

Marks KU | PS

7. A student made the following statements about the particles found in an atom.

A	Relative mass = 1
B	Charge = zero
C	Found outside the nucleus
D	Charge = 1+
E	Charge = 1−

Identify the **two** statements which apply to an electron.

A
B
C
D
E

(1)

[Turn over

8. Identify the **two** statements which apply to zinc.

You may wish to use the data booklet to help you.

A	It displaces calcium from a solution of calcium nitrate.
B	It reacts with cold water.
C	It can be obtained by heating its oxide.
D	It reacts with dilute hydrochloric acid.
E	It is displaced from a solution of its chloride by magnesium.

| A |
| B |
| C |
| D |
| E |

(2)

9. The diagram shows how an object can be coated with silver.

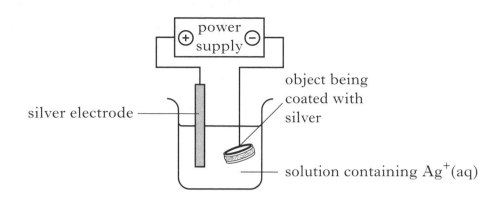

The following reactions take place at the electrodes.

Negative electrode: $Ag^+(aq) + e^- \longrightarrow Ag(s)$

Positive electrode: $Ag(s) \longrightarrow Ag^+(aq) + e^-$

Identify the **two** correct statements.

A	Ions flow through the solution.
B	Silver ions move towards the silver electrode.
C	The process is an example of galvanising.
D	The mass of the silver electrode decreases.
E	Reduction occurs at the silver electrode.

A
B
C
D
E

(2)

[Turn over

Marks

10. A student made the following statements about the rusting of iron.

A	During rusting Fe^{3+} ions are changed to Fe^{2+} ions.
B	Rusting is an example of oxidation.
C	Iron rusts when connected to the negative terminal of a battery.
D	Tin gives sacrificial protection to iron.
E	Electroplating provides a surface barrier to air and water.

Identify the **two** correct statements.

| A |
| B |
| C |
| D |
| E |

(2)

[Turn over for Part 2 on *Page fourteen*

Marks KU PS

PART 2

A total of 40 marks is available in this part of the paper.

11. (*a*) The table shows information about two of the gases found in air.

Gas	Boiling point/°C
oxygen	−183
nitrogen	−196

At very low temperatures air is a mixture of liquids.

Name the process which can be used to separate this mixture.

_____   1

(*b*) In a sample of oxygen there are two different types of oxygen atom:

$^{18}_{8}O$ and $^{16}_{8}O$

(i) What **term** is used to describe these different types of oxygen atom?

_____   1

(ii) Complete the table for each type of oxygen atom.

Type of atom	Number of protons	Number of neutrons
$^{18}_{8}O$		
$^{16}_{8}O$		

1

(3)

Marks

KU	PS

12. (a) Ethanol, for alcoholic drinks, can be made from glucose.

Name this process.

_____ **1**

(b) The table below shows the relationship between the percentage of ethanol and the density of alcoholic drinks.

Percentage of ethanol (%)	40	50	60	70	80
Density of alcoholic drink (g/cm^3)	0·928	0·907	0·886	0·865	0·844

(i) Write a general statement describing how the percentage of ethanol affects the density of the alcoholic drink.

_____

_____

_____ **1**

(ii) The density of a particular brand of alcoholic drink is $0·970 \, \text{g/cm}^3$.

Predict the percentage of ethanol in this alcoholic drink.

_____ % **1**

(3)

[Turn over

13. Polyvinyldichloride (PVDC) is a plastic used in food packaging.

The structure of part of a PVDC molecule is shown.

```
     Cl  H  Cl  H  Cl  H
      |  |   |  |   |  |
   -  C -C - C -C - C -C -
      |  |   |  |   |  |
     Cl  H  Cl  H  Cl  H
```

(a) Draw the **full** structural formula for the monomer used to make PVDC.

1

(b) Name a toxic gas produced when PVDC burns.

_____

1

(2)

Marks | KU | PS

14. (a) When sulphur dioxide dissolves in water in the atmosphere "acid rain" is produced.

Circle the correct phrase to complete the sentence.

Compared with pure water, acid rain contains $\begin{cases} \text{a higher} \\ \text{a lower} \\ \text{the same} \end{cases}$ concentration of hydrogen ions. **1**

(b) The table shows information about the solubility of sulphur dioxide.

Temperature /°C	0	20	30	40	50	60
Solubility in g/100 cm³	22·0	10·0	6·0	3·0	2·0	1·5

Draw a line graph of solubility against temperature.

Use appropriate scales to fill most of the graph paper.

(Additional graph paper, if required, will be found on page 28.)

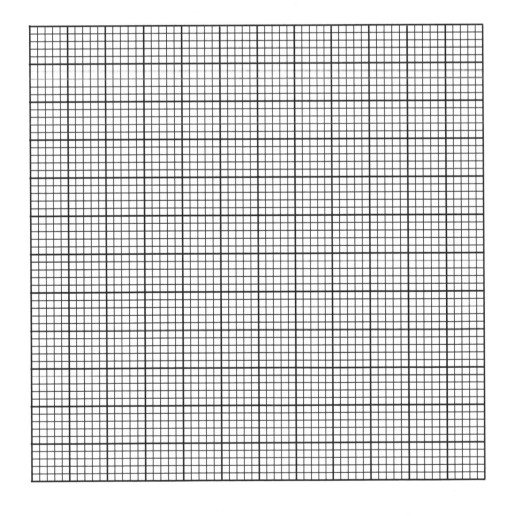

2

(3)

Marks

15. Scientists have developed a "bio-battery" which produces electricity from sucrose.

(*a*) Write the molecular formula for sucrose.

1

(*b*) Name an isomer of sucrose.

_____

1

(*c*) The sucrose is broken down using an enzyme.

(i) What is meant by the term "enzyme"?

_____

1

(ii) The graph shows how temperature affects the activity of an enzyme.

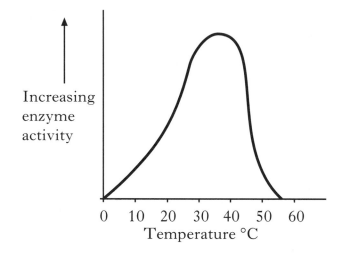

State **one** other factor which has a similar effect on enzyme activity.

_____

1

(4)

Marks

16. Heptane can be cracked as shown.

One of the reactions which takes place is:

$$C_7H_{16} \longrightarrow C_4H_{10} + C_3H_6$$

(a) The product C_3H_6 decolourises bromine solution quickly.

Draw a structural formula for an isomer of C_3H_6, which would **not** decolourise bromine solution quickly.

1

(b) Aluminium oxide is used as a catalyst to speed up the reaction.

(i) Suggest another reason for using a catalyst.

_____

_____

1

(ii) Write the formula for aluminium oxide.

1

(3)

[**Turn over**

DO NOT WRITE IN THIS MARGIN

Marks

	KU	PS

17. Urea reacts with water, breaking down to form carbon dioxide and ammonia.

$$H_2NCONH_2 \; + \; H_2O \longrightarrow CO_2 \; + \; 2NH_3$$

urea

(a) Suggest a name for the **type** of chemical reaction taking place.

_____   1

(b) Calculate the mass of ammonia produced, in grams, when 90 g of urea breaks down.

_____ g   2

(3)

Marks KU PS

18. A student set up the following experiment to electrolyse cobalt chloride solution.

power supply

electrodes   +   −

cobalt chloride
solution

(a) What **type** of power supply **must** be used to electrolyse cobalt chloride solution?

_____   1

(b) Describe what would be **seen** at the positive electrode.

You may wish to use the data booklet to help you.

_____

_____   1

(c) The formula for cobalt chloride is $CoCl_2$.

What is the charge on the cobalt ion in $CoCl_2$?

_____   1

(3)

[Turn over

19. Catalysts can be used in different processes.

(a) The flow diagram shows the steps involved in the Haber process.

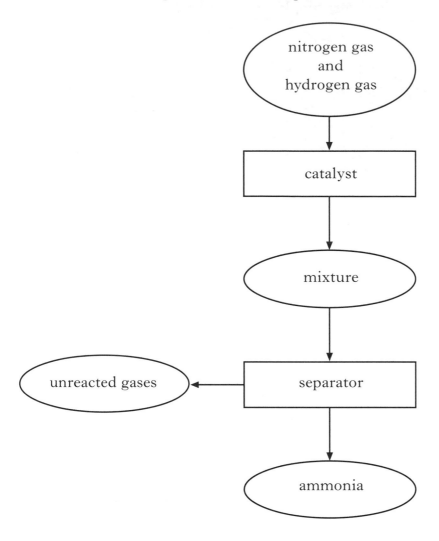

On the flow diagram above draw an arrow to show how the process is made more economical.

1

Marks

19. (continued)

(*b*) Ammonia can be used to produce nitrogen dioxide as shown.

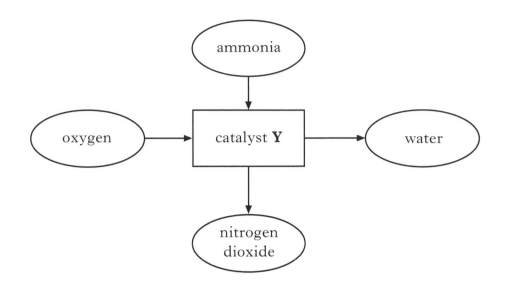

(i) Name catalyst **Y**.

_____   1

(ii) Why is it **not** necessary to continue to supply heat once the reaction has started?

_____

_____   1

(*c*) Catalysts are also used in catalytic converters.

What is the purpose of a catalytic converter in a car exhaust system?

_____

_____

_____   1

(4)

[Turn over

Marks

20. Metal salts can be produced by different methods.

(a) Lead(II) iodide can be produced by reacting lead(II) nitrate solution with sodium iodide solution.

The equation for this reaction is:

$$Pb(NO_3)_2(aq) \ + \ NaI(aq) \longrightarrow PbI_2(s) \ + \ NaNO_3(aq)$$

   (i) Balance the above equation.

1

   (ii) What technique could be used to remove lead(II) iodide from the mixture?

_____

1

(b) The salt copper(II) nitrate can be produced as shown.

$$\mathbf{X} \ + \ 2HNO_3 \longrightarrow Cu(NO_3)_2 \ + \ CO_2 \ + \ H_2O$$

Name substance **X**.

_____

1

(c) Potassium sulphate can be produced by titrating potassium hydroxide solution with dilute sulphuric acid.

burette containing 0·1 mol/l sulphuric acid

conical flask

10 cm³ potassium hydroxide solution

Marks

KU | PS

20. **(c) (continued)**

(i) What must be added to the conical flask to show the end-point of the titration?

_____ **1**

(ii) The average volume of sulphuric acid used in the titration is $20\,cm^3$.

Calculate the number of moles of sulphuric acid used.

_____ mol **1**

(d) The equation for the reaction is:

$$H_2SO_4 \;+\; 2KOH \longrightarrow K_2SO_4 \;+\; 2H_2O$$

Using your answer from part (c)(ii), calculate the number of moles of potassium hydroxide in the $10\,cm^3$ sample of potassium hydroxide solution.

_____ mol **1**

(6)

[Turn over

Marks | KU | PS

21. A technician set up the following cell.

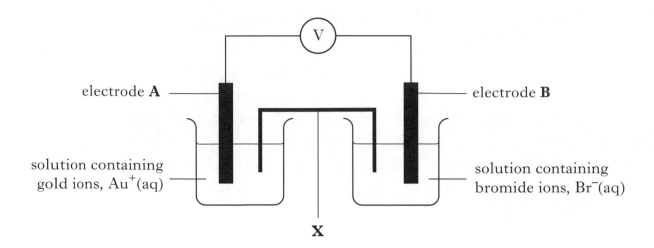

The reaction taking place at electrode **B** is:

$$2Br^-(aq) \longrightarrow Br_2(\ell) + 2e^-$$

(a) **On the diagram**, clearly mark the path and direction of electron flow.   1

(b) Write the ion-electron equation for the reaction taking place at electrode **A**.

You may wish to use the data booklet to help you.

   1

(c) Name the piece of apparatus labelled **X**.

_____   1

(3)

DO NOT
WRITE IN
THIS
MARGIN

Marks | KU | PS

22. Ethylthioethane belongs to a homologous series of compounds called thioethers.

(a) What is meant by a homologous series?

_____

_____

_____   1

(b) Ethylthioethane is formed when ethylthiol reacts with bromoethane as shown.

$$H-\underset{\underset{H}{|}}{\overset{\overset{H}{|}}{C}}-\underset{\underset{H}{|}}{\overset{\overset{H}{|}}{C}}-S-H \;+\; Br-\underset{\underset{H}{|}}{\overset{\overset{H}{|}}{C}}-\underset{\underset{H}{|}}{\overset{\overset{H}{|}}{C}}-H \longrightarrow H-\underset{\underset{H}{|}}{\overset{\overset{H}{|}}{C}}-\underset{\underset{H}{|}}{\overset{\overset{H}{|}}{C}}-S-\underset{\underset{H}{|}}{\overset{\overset{H}{|}}{C}}-\underset{\underset{H}{|}}{\overset{\overset{H}{|}}{C}}-H \;+\; HBr$$

ethylthiol   bromoethane   ethylthioethane   hydrogen
                                                                        bromide

Draw the **full** structural formula for the thioether produced in the following reaction.

$$H-\underset{\underset{H}{|}}{\overset{\overset{H}{|}}{C}}-S-H \;+\; Br-\underset{\underset{H}{|}}{\overset{\overset{H}{|}}{C}}-\underset{\underset{H}{|}}{\overset{\overset{H}{|}}{C}}-\underset{\underset{H}{|}}{\overset{\overset{H}{|}}{C}}-H \longrightarrow \boxed{} \;+\; HBr$$

1

(c) Ethylthioethane can also be formed by the reaction of ethylthiol with ethene.

$$H-\underset{\underset{H}{|}}{\overset{\overset{H}{|}}{C}}-\underset{\underset{H}{|}}{\overset{\overset{H}{|}}{C}}-S-H \;+\; \overset{H}{\underset{H}{\diagdown}}C=C\overset{H}{\underset{H}{\diagup}} \longrightarrow H-\underset{\underset{H}{|}}{\overset{\overset{H}{|}}{C}}-\underset{\underset{H}{|}}{\overset{\overset{H}{|}}{C}}-S-\underset{\underset{H}{|}}{\overset{\overset{H}{|}}{C}}-\underset{\underset{H}{|}}{\overset{\overset{H}{|}}{C}}-H$$

ethylthiol   ethene   ethylthioethane

Suggest a name for the **type** of chemical reaction taking place.

_____   1

(3)

[END OF QUESTION PAPER]

ADDITIONAL SPACE FOR ANSWERS

ADDITIONAL GRAPH PAPER FOR QUESTION 14(*b*)

ADDITIONAL SPACE FOR ANSWERS

ADDITIONAL SPACE FOR ANSWERS

[BLANK PAGE]

Acknowledgements

Permission has been sought from all relevant copyright holders and Bright Red Publishing is grateful for the use of the following:

A drawing of a BMW car © BMW (2007 Credit page 18).

STANDARD GRADE | ANSWER SECTION

CHEMISTRY CREDIT
2007

PART 1

1. (a) A   (b) D

2. (a) A   (b) B and C

3. (a) E   (b) A

4. (a) F   (b) B and D

5. (a) C   (b) F

6. (a) E   (b) C   (c) A and D

7. D and E

8. C and E

9. B and D

PART 2

10. (a) Equal amounts/same amount/50:50

(b)

Particle	Number
proton	47
neutron	60
electron	46

(c) (i) $2AgNO_3 + Cu \rightarrow 2Ag + Cu(NO_3)_2$
    (ii)   Mercury or gold or platinum

11. (a)

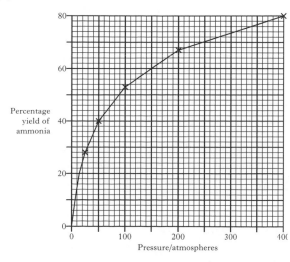

(b) (i)   Boiling point increases as the number of (carbon) atoms increases

    or

    As the (carbon) atom number increases the boiling point increases.

    (ii)   175–193

12. (a)

Percentage yield of ammonia vs Pressure/atmospheres

(b) 60 ± 1

(c) alkali/a hydroxide/base

13. (a) Glucose and fructose

(b) Biological catalyst/enzyme/acid

14. (a) Negative

(b) (i)   Galvanising

    (ii)   Zinc is more reactive

        or
        Zinc is higher up in the electrochemical series/reactivity series
        or
        Zinc provides sacrificial protection
        or
        Electrons flow to iron
        or
        Zinc gives electrons to iron/Zinc provides electrons.
        or
        Zinc sacrifices itself.
        or
        Zinc sacrificially oxidises.

15. (a) $H:\ddot{C}l:$

(b) To form full/complete/stable electron shell/circle/level
    or
    To become stable
    or
    To get same electron arrangement as a noble gas
    or
    To have a stable octet
    or
    To get 8 electrons in outer level
    or
    To be like a noble gas
    or
    To become more stable

16. (a) (i)   Fermentation/Anaerobic respiration
       (ii)   Slows down/decreases/stop/will not work/goes to zero

(b) (i)   Addition or hydration
    (ii)   Isomers
    (iii)   Distillation

17. (a) Zinc sulphide

(b) Aluminium chloride **or** $AlCl_3$ **or** $Al^{3+}(Cl^-)_3$

(c) 51·3

(d) $Fe_2O_3 + CO \rightarrow Fe + CO_2$

(e) Gold **or** mercury **or** silver **or** platinum

18. (a) Reshaped / moulded / softens on heating / on melting. Flexes when heated.

(b) Condensation

19. (a) Colourless

(b) $Ni^{2+}(NO_3^-)_2$

(c) (i)   Yellow
    (ii)   Allow ions to move/flow
        or
        Completes the circuit/finish circuit
    (iii)   Insoluble

20. (a) 0·2

(b) (i) 0·1

(ii) 10

CHEMISTRY CREDIT 2008

PART 1

1. (a) C   (b) B   (c) D

2. (a) A and F   (b) B

3. (a) C and D   (b) B and F

4. (a) D and F   (b) E   (c) C

5. (a) D   (b) A and C

6. D

7. (a) A and B   (b) E

8. C and E

9. B and E

PART 2

10. (a) Halogen

(b) A covalent bond forms when two _positive_ nuclei are held together by their common attaction for a shared pair of _electrons_.

(c) As the size increases the amount of energy decreases / as the size decreases the energy increases **or** The energy required decreases as the size increases. / the energy required increases as the size decreases

11. (a) Hydroxide/OH$^-$

(b) Increase/speed it up

(c) Sacrificial

12. (a) (i)

(ii) 13

(b) $NaN_3 \rightarrow 1\frac{1}{2} N_2 + Na$

or $2NaN_3 \rightarrow 3N_2 + 2Na$

(c) Unreactive/will not react with sodium/does not burn/not flammable

13. (a) Conducts electricity/conductor

(b) $2Cl^- \rightarrow Cl_2 + 2e$

(c) Ions are free to move

14. (*a*) Carbon, hydrogen, oxygen

(*b*) Sucrose

(*c*) 0·0033

15. (*a*) (i) 1
(ii) Electron

(*b*) (i) proton 90
neutron 144
(ii) 84

16. (*a*) 68·3

(*b*) Aluminium - electrolysis of molten compound
Lead - using heat and carbon

(*c*) Less reactive/lower in reactivity series

(*d*) Reduction

17. (*a*) (i) No reaction
(ii) Reaction occurred

(*b*) (i) NO_3^-
(ii) Filtration/filtering or correct description

18. (*a*) Lightning

(*b*) Bacteria **or** nitrogen-fixing bacteria
or nitrifying bacteria

(*c*) Ammonia/NH_3

(*d*) As the temperature increases/*decreases* the solubility
decreases/*increases* **or**

The solubility increases/*decreases*, as the temperature
decreases/*increases*.

19. (*a*)

(*b*) Isomers

(*c*) 20–27

20. (*a*) 28 g

(*b*) 3^+/three positive/Fe^{3+}

(*c*) (i) *Any one from:*
• To provide/supply oxygen
• To produce carbon dioxide/monoxide
• To provide oxygen to react with carbon
• For combustion to take place

(ii) Iron would be solid/harden/solidify
Iron would not be able to flow/molten/liquid

CHEMISTRY CREDIT 2009

PART 1

1. (*a*) A   (*b*) F

2. (*a*) D   (*b*) F

3. (*a*) B   (*b*) D

4. (*a*) C   (*b*) A and C   (*c*) F

5. (*a*) B and E   (*b*) C   (*c*) B and F

6. (*a*) E   (*b*) C   (*c*) B and D

7. A and F

8. C and D

PART 2

9. (*a*) 10   10
10   11
10   12

(*b*) Isotopes

(*c*) 20 or ^{20}Ne

10. (*a*) Electrolysis

(*b*) $(Al^{3+})_2(O^{2-})_3 Al_2^{3+} O_3^{2-}$

(*c*) Ions can move/free ions
Ionic lattice broken up

11. (*a*) Hydrogen or H or H_2
Carbon or C

(*b*) Test tube A – colourless liquid or water or H_2O
– condensation
Test tube B – lime water did not turn milky or no change

12. (*a*) Covalent

(*b*) Diagram must show 1 P and 3 H atoms
3 pairs of shared electrons and 2 non-bonded electrons

13. (*a*) Neutralisation

(*b*) (i) Gas given off/CO_2 given off

(ii) Both scales correct
Both labels correct including units
Plots correct
Joining points

(*c*) Greater than 0.8
No higher than 0.86

14. (*a*) (i) Ostwald

(ii) Reaction is exothermic/gives out heat
It is exothermic

(iii) Water/H_2O

(*b*) FM = 80

$$\% = \frac{28 \times 100}{80} = 35$$

15. (*a*) Y   X   W   Z

(*b*) Hydrogen/H_2

(*c*) Y = K/Na/Li/Ca/Mg
Z = Hg/Ag/Au/Pt

16. (a) Hydrolysis

(b) $C_6H_{12}O_6 \longrightarrow 2\ C_2H_5OH + 2\ CO_2$

(c) distillation
evaporation **and** condensation

(d) FM = 46

$$\frac{230}{46} = 5$$

17. (a) Oxidation

(b) Right to left (Y to X)
On or very close to wire
Not nearer to ion bridge

(c) Add starch
Blue-black

(d) $Br_2 + 2e \longrightarrow 2Br^-$

18. (a)

(b) Carbon = 8 hydrogen = 17

(c) Carbon monoxide or CO
Hydrogen cyanide or HCN

19. (a) 216 – 221 inclusive

(b) Homologous

(c) 1 mol $\longrightarrow$ 10 mol

128 $\longrightarrow$ 180

6·4 $\longrightarrow$ $\dfrac{6\cdot4 \times 180}{128} = 9$

(d) Correct structural formula for butane

CHEMISTRY CREDIT 2010

PART 1

1. (a) E   (b) A

2. (a) E   (b) A and C   (c) D and F

3. (a) A and D   (b) D

4. (a) E   (b) A and B

5. (a) B   (b) D

6. (a) B and F   (b) B   (c) E and F

7. (a) D   (b) C

8.   B and E

9.   A and F

PART 2

10. (a) Human made **or**
Man made/unnatural/not natural

(b) (i)

(ii) Addition

(c) Carbon monoxide/CO

11. (a) (i) Fermentation/anaerobic respiration
(ii) Carbon dioxide/CO_2

(b) The balloon does not inflate/inflates less/not as much

12. (a) Burns with a pop

(b)

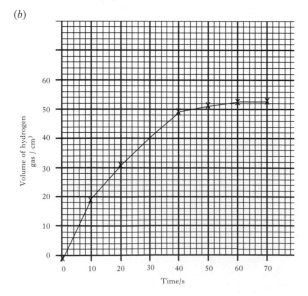

(c) 41 +/-1

(d) 53

(*e*) 1 mol   1 mol
24·5   2
4·9   0·4

or

n =   m/gfm
=   4·9/24·5
=   0·2

1 mol → 1 mol
0·2 mol → 0·2 mol

m = $n \times$ gfm
=   0·2 × 2
=   0·4 g

13. (*a*) To allow the products to be identified/separated/ only one product/colour is collected at an electrode

or

To allow colours to be separated/identified

(*b*) Green

(*c*) Ni^{2+} CrO_4^{2-}

14. (*a*) Covalent

(*b*) (i) $TiCl_4 + 4Na \rightarrow Ti + 4NaCl$
(ii) Titanium is less reactive **or**
Sodium is more reactive

15. (*a*) As the distance from the surface *increases* the concentration *increases.*/As the distance from the surface decreases the concentration decreases.

or

The concentration increases as the distance increases./
The concentration decreases as the distance decreases.

(*b*) 80·5

(*c*) (protons)   (electrons)   (both required)

16. (*a*) (i) 2+/two positive **or**
+2/positive 2
(ii) gfm = 239
207/239 × 100 = 86·6
86·6% (87%)

(*b*) (i) Iron/Fe
(ii) Mercury   Hg
Aluminium   Al
Copper   Cu   (all 3 required)

17. (*a*) (NO_3^-)

(*b*) Ferroxyl indicator turns blue

(*c*) $Ag^+ + e^- \rightarrow Ag$
$2Ag^+ + 2e^- \rightarrow 2Ag$

(*d*)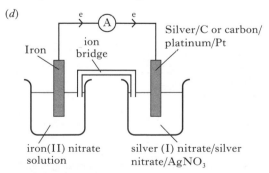

18. (*a*) Ethoxypropane

(*b*) (approximately) 36°C (32–40°C)

19. (*a*) 25 cm³

(*b*) n = $c \times v$
=   0·1 × 0·025
=   0·0025 mol HCl

1 : 1
0·0025 : 0·0025 mol NaOH

c =   n/v

= $\dfrac{0·0025}{0·01}$

=   0·25 mol/l NaOH

c = $\dfrac{n/m}{v}$ = zero

or

$OH^- \times v \times c$ = $H^+ \times v \times c$
$1 \times 10 \times$ conc = $1 \times 25 \times 0·1$

conc = $\dfrac{1 \times 25 \times 0·1}{1 \times 10}$

=   0·25 mol/l

20. (*a*) (i) Propanol **or** propan-1-ol

(ii)

or

(*b*) Carbon dioxide/CO_2
Water/H_2O/hydrogen oxide

CHEMISTRY CREDIT 2011

PART 1

1. B

2. (a) E   (b) A

3. (a) A   (b) B and C   (c) C and D

4. (a) F   (b) A and F

5. (a) B and F   (b) C   (c) E

6. (a) D   (b) B

7. C and E

8. D and E

9. A and D

10. B and E

PART 2

11. (a) Distillation/fractional distillation
   Evaporation then condensation

   (b) (i) Isotopes

      (ii) 8   10
          8   8

12. (a) Fermentation
   Anaerobic respiration

   (b) (i) As the percentage increases...the density decreases
         As the percentage decreases...the density increases

      (ii) 20

13. (a)

   or

   (b) Hydrogen chloride, HCl
   Carbon monoxide

14. (a) a higher

(b)
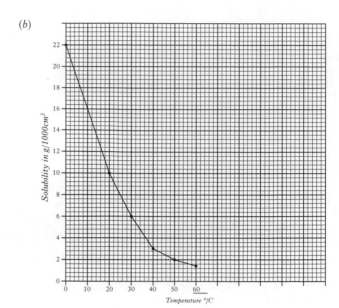

Both labels with units – ½ mark
Both scales – ½ mark
Plots correct – ½ mark
Plots joined – ½ mark

15. (a) $C_{12}H_{22}O_{11}$

   (b) Maltose
   Lactose

   (c) (i) Biological catalyst

      (ii) pH
         Acidity or Alkalinity
         Concentration of acid
         Concentration of alkali

16. (a) Full or shortened structural formula of cyclopropane
   eg

   (b) (i) Lower temperature
         Less heat/energy

      (ii) Al_2O_3
         If ion charges are shown all must be correct
         $(Al^{3+})_2 (O^{2-})_3 / Al^{3+}_2 O^{2-}_3$

17. (a) hydrolysis

   (b) 1mol   2mol

       60   34

       90       $\dfrac{90 \times 34}{60} =$ 51

18. (a) d.c. or direct current

   (b) Chlorine gas
   Bubbles of gas
   Gas given off
   Fizzing/effervescence
   Green/yellow gas
   Cl_2 (g)

   (c) Two positive,   2+, Co^{2+}

19. (a) Arrows drawn from unreacted gases to hydrogen and
   nitrogen box or catalyst box or between these two

   (b) (i) Platinum, Pt

      (ii) It is an exothermic reaction
         The reaction produces heat

(c) Convert pollutant gases to harmless gases
Convert harmful gases to harmless gases

$$CO \longrightarrow CO_2 \quad \textbf{or}$$
$$NO_X \longrightarrow N_2$$

20. (a) (i) $Pb(NO_3)_2(aq) + 2NaI(aq) \longrightarrow PbI_2(s) + 2NaNO_3(aq)$

(ii) filtration

(b)   Copper carbonate $CuCO_3$

(c) (i) Indicator/named acid/base indicator

(ii) Moles $n = c \times v$
$$= 0.1 \times 0.02 \text{ moles}$$
$$= 0.002 \text{ moles}$$

(d) Apply mole ratio
$$0.002 \longrightarrow 0.004$$

21. (a) A $\longleftarrow$ B

(b) $Au^+(aq) + e^- \longrightarrow Au(s)$

(c) Ion bridge/salt bridge
Filter paper soaked in salt solution/electrolyte

22. (a) Same general formula and same/similar properties/same/similar chemical properties

(b)

(c)   addition